Einstein's Relativity and the Quantum Revolution: Modern Physics for Non-Scientists

Part I

Professor Richard Wolfson

THE TEACHING COMPANY ®

PUBLISHED BY:

THE TEACHING COMPANY
4151 Lafayette Center Drive, Suite 100
Chantilly, Virginia 20151-1232
1-800-TEACH-12
Fax – 703-378-3819
www.teach12.com

ISBN 1-56585-612-0

Richard Wolfson, Ph.D.

Professor of Physics, Middlebury College

Richard Wolfson is Professor of Physics at Middlebury College, where he has also held the George Adams Ellis Chair in the Liberal Arts. He did undergraduate work at MIT and Swarthmore College, graduating from Swarthmore with a double major in physics and philosophy. He holds a master's degree in environmental studies from the University of Michigan and a Ph.D. in physics from Dartmouth College. His published research includes such diverse fields as medical physics, plasma physics, solar energy engineering, electronic circuit design, observational astronomy, and theoretical astrophysics. Professor Wolfson's current research involves the sometimes violently eruptive behavior of the Sun's outer atmosphere, or corona. He also continues an interest in environmental science, especially global climate change. As a college professor, Wolfson is particularly interested in making physics relevant to students from all walks of academic life. His textbook, *Physics for Scientists and Engineers* (Addison Wesley, 1999), is now in its third edition and has been translated into several foreign languages. Wolfson is also an interpreter of science for nonscientists; he has published in *Scientific American* and wrote *Nuclear Choices: A Citizen's Guide to Nuclear Technology* (MIT Press, 1993). The original version of this course on physics was produced in 1995, and in 1996, Wolfson produced another Teaching Company course, *Energy and Climate: Science for Citizens in the Age of Global Warming*. Although he has been at Middlebury for his entire post-Ph.D. career, Professor Wolfson has spent sabbaticals at the National Center for Atmospheric Research in Boulder, Colorado; at St. Andrews University in Scotland; and at Stanford University.

Table of Contents

Einstein's Relativity and the Quantum Revolution: Modern Physics for Non-Scientists
Part I

Einstein's Relativity and the Quantum Revolution: Modern Physics for Non-Scientists

Scope:

The twentieth century brought two revolutionary changes in humankind's understanding of the physical universe in which we live. These revolutions—relativity and the quantum theory—touch the very basis of physical reality, altering our commonsense notions of space and time, cause and effect. The revolutionary nature of these ideas endows them with implications well beyond physics; indeed, philosophical debate continues to this day, especially over the meaning of quantum physics.

Is time travel to the future possible? You bet—but if you don't like what you find, you can't come back! Are there really such bizarre objects as black holes that warp space and time so much that not even light can escape? Almost certainly! And do the even weirder cousins of black holes, wormholes, exist—perhaps affording us shortcuts to remote reaches of space and time? Quite possibly! Is the universe governed by laws that strictly predict exactly what will happen in the future or is it governed by chance? In part, by chance! All these and other equally strange consequences flow from relativity and quantum physics.

Many people think that relativity and quantum physics must be far beyond their comprehension. Indeed, how many times have you heard it said of something difficult that "it would take an Einstein to understand that"? To grasp these new descriptions of physical reality in all their mathematical detail is indeed daunting. But the basic ideas behind relativity and quantum physics are, in fact, simple and comprehensible by anyone; for example, a single, concise English sentence suffices to state Einstein's theory of relativity.

This course presents the fundamental ideas of relativity and quantum physics in twenty-four lectures intended for interested people who need have no background whatsoever in science or mathematics. Following a brief history of humankind's thinking about physical reality, the lectures outline rigorously the logic that led inexorably to Einstein's special theory of relativity. After an exploration of the implications of special relativity, we move on to Einstein's general theory of relativity and its interpretation of gravity in terms of the curving of space and time. We see how the Hubble Space Telescope provides some of the most striking confirmations of general relativity, including near-certain confirmation of the existence of black holes. Then we explore quandaries that arose as physicists began probing the heart of matter at the atomic and subatomic scales, quandaries that led even the great physicist Werner Heisenberg to wonder "can nature possibly be as absurd as it seems to us in these atomic experiments?" The resolution of those quandaries is the quantum theory, a vision of physical reality so at odds with our experience that even our language fails to describe the quantum world. After a brief exposition of quantum theory, we explore the "zoo" of particles and forces that, at the most fundamental level, comprise everything, including ourselves. We then bring together our understanding of physical reality at the smallest and largest scales to provide a picture of the origin, evolution, and possible futures of the entire universe and our place in it. Finally, we consider the possibility that physics may produce a "theory of everything," explaining all aspects of the physical universe.

A first version of this course was first produced in 1995. In this new 1999 version, I have chosen to spend more time on the philosophical interpretation of quantum physics and on recent experiments relevant to that interpretation. I have also added a final lecture on the "theory of everything" and its possible implementation through string theory. The graphic presentations for the video version have also been extensively revised and enhanced. But the goal remains the same: to present the key ideas of modern physics in a way that makes them clear to the interested layperson.

Lecture One

Time Travel, Tunneling, Tennis, and Tea

Scope:

The two big ideas of modern physics are relativity and quantum physics. Relativity radically alters our notions of space and time, while quantum physics reveals a universe governed ultimately not by strict determinism but, in part, by pure chance. Modern physics stands in contrast to classical physics, developed before 1900 but still applicable to everyday phenomena. Although modern physics forces radical changes in our philosophical thinking about the physical world, the basic ideas of modern physics are nevertheless accessible to nonscientists.

Outline

I. Two impossible tales—or are they impossible?

    A. The tale of the twins: They start out the same age; one makes a high-speed round-trip journey to a distant star while the other stays home on Earth. When the traveling twin returns, they're different ages!

    B. Escape from prison by quantum tunneling: You're trapped in a concrete-walled prison cell. You pace back and forth all day, confined by the walls. Suddenly, you find yourself on the outside!

II. The nature of physics.

    A. What is physics?

        1. Physics is the subject that describes our physical environment, from the smallest subatomic particles to the entire universe.

        2. Physics is important to everyone, not just physicists!

    B. Classical versus modern physics.

        1. Classical physics is the realm of physics developed before 1900, which is still applicable to most everyday phenomena (such as driving a car, engineering a skyscraper, designing a telescope, launching a satellite, generating electric power, predicting weather and planetary motion, and so on).

2. Modern physics has been developed in the twentieth century and describes phenomena at very small (i.e., atomic) scales or when relative speeds approach that of light. This course is about the two big ideas at the heart of modern physics.

C. The two big ideas of modern physics.

1. Relativity, developed largely by Einstein beginning in 1905, is a great equalizer. It asserts that everyone experiences the same laws of physics, regardless of their location or state of motion.

2. In this way, relativity builds on the Copernican notion that Earth does not occupy a privileged position in the universe. Despite its simple content, relativity radically bends and blends our notions of time and space.

3. Quantum physics reveals a noncontinuously dividable, or "grainy," universe at the smallest scales and with it, bids farewell to strict determinism.

4. In other words, at the fundamental levels of matter, causation is a matter of statistical probabilities, not certainties.

D. Physics is a human activity, which most scientists nevertheless believe is a quest toward understanding an underlying objective reality. Developing new ideas of physics, especially with fundamentals such as relativity and quantum physics, is often more like a creative artistic process than the stereotypical "scientific method" emphasized in school science courses.

III. It doesn't take an Einstein to understand modern physics! The goal of this course is to make the key ideas of modern physics accessible, comprehensible, and even simple for the interested nonscientist.

A. For example, you can play tennis, or brew a cup of tea, equally at home, on a cruise ship, on Venus, or on a planet in a distant galaxy.

B. Trivial as this example is, understanding it means grasping and accepting the essential idea of Einstein's relativity, namely, that the laws that govern physical reality are the same everywhere in the universe.

Essential Reading:

Hoffmann, *Relativity and Its Roots*, Chapter 1.

Questions to Consider:

1. Articulate why it is, in terms of your own understanding of time, that you find the example of the time-traveling twins disturbing.

2. Why do you suppose it is that you don't have to take into account the ship's motion in the example of playing tennis on a cruise ship?

Lecture One—Transcript
Time Travel, Tunneling, Tennis, and Tea

Welcome to *Einstein's Relativity and the Quantum Revolution: A Course in Modern Physics for Non-Scientists*. I'm Professor Rich Wolfson from Middlebury College. And before I begin, I'd just like to say a little about my title, to emphasize two terms in that title. First of all, the term modern physics. This is a course in the great ideas that shaped the physics of the twentieth- and twenty-first centuries. It's not a course in all of physics. And it's not a course in the really latest, most contemporary ideas, although we will touch on those. Rather, it's a course in the true, fundamental ideas that set the tone for all the physics that's occurred since the year 1900.

Before I describe the course and give you a brief introduction, I'd like to tell you two stories that give you a sense of what modern physics is about and how radically it's reshaped our notions of the physical universe, in particular our notions of space and time and causality.

The first involves a couple of twins. Imagine you are a twin, and you're 20 years old—in your youth—and you have a twin sister. And you and your twin sister go out in the backyard and you build a space ship. And on your 20th birthday, your twin sister hops in the space ship and travels off to a distant star. And she goes out there, and she spends some time exploring that star—and you wait, and you wait, and you wait. And eventually your twin sister returns, and you find the time of her return is your 80th birthday. So she has been away for 60 years. And here comes the space ship, and it lands back in your backyard, and out hops your twin sister, and she's a youthful 25. Five years have elapsed for her. Sixty years have elapsed for you. In some sense she's time traveled into your future. And that is the first phrase in the title of this lecture, "Time Travel, Tunneling, Tennis, and Tea," because one of the things that modern physics seems to make possible is time travel, at least into the future in the sense I've just described in the story of the two twins.

Is this really possible? Could it really happen? Is time so strange that two twins who start out at age 20, together, can find themselves later 55 years apart? The answer is, yes. We've confirmed this with subatomic particles. We've even confirmed it with real-sized clocks, although there the time difference was billionths of a second instead of decades. But this happens. It can happen, and it tells us something remarkable about the nature of time.

Let me tell you another seemingly impossible story that relates to the second phrase in my title. Again, the title of this lecture, "Time Travel, Tunneling, Tennis, and Tea." This is the phrase, "Tunneling." Imagine you are stuck in a prison. You have concrete walls on all sides. You're trapped there. You're in for a long sentence. And so, what do you do? Well, you have nothing to do, but you pace back and forth. And occasionally you lean up against those hard concrete walls of your prison. Of course, you can't get out. And then one day, when you're leaning against the walls of the prison, you suddenly find yourself on the outside. You've somehow inexorably penetrated a seemingly impenetrable barrier. Is this possible? It seems not. Not according to anything your common sense tells you.

In fact, it's the phenomenon of quantum tunneling. Again, we've verified it. Again, with subatomic particles. We believe, in principle, it could happen in other circumstances, but we have not seen it happen, and it's very unlikely that it would happen with a macroscopic sized object like a prisoner. But it definitely happens with subatomic particles. In fact, we're alive today because protons in the core of the sun tunnel through an insurmountable barrier—analogous to that concrete wall of the prison—and are able to get together and fuse to make helium, and in the process releasing the energy, which tens of thousands of years later emerges from the surface of the sun as sunlight, and eight minutes after that reaches Earth, and is the energy that sustains life on our planet. So, this is a real phenomenon, and it's one on which our lives directly depend.

Those are two stories of seemingly impossible events. And yet, they're events that occur. They could occur as I've described them—although are unlikely or difficult to make happen—they do occur regularly in the subatomic realm. They're ideas that suggest to us that our basic common sense notions of time, of space, and of what it means to be rigid and solid and insurmountable are all in some way compromised, or modified, or extended, or enriched by the ideas of modern physics. So, there are some stories. And we'll come to understand how both those things are possible in the course of this lecture series.

Let me pause now and say a little bit about what physics is. People have a lot of misconceptions about physics. I often tell people I'm a physics professor. And they say, "Oh, physics," and they kind of think that's something for a rarefied breed of people who occupy specialized laboratories and think about things that have nothing to do with what's important to the common person. Actually, nothing could be further from the truth. Physics is the essence of the way the physical universe works. We live in the physical universe, like it or not. We walk. We drive cars. We fly airplanes. We have weather happen to us. We swim. We turn on water. We cook. All these basic, everyday processes involve the fundamental laws of physics. Physics is the fundamental science. The laws of physics underline everything that goes on in the physical universe.

Physics is not just for physicists. It's not just for people who occupy laboratories and invent bizarre new devices or think about esoteric thoughts like time travel, for example. Physics is for everyone, because physics is the essence of what most of us do—in fact, what all of us do all of the time. In fact, I'm going to give you another example at the end of this lecture, which will convince you that you already know a lot more physics than you think. In fact, you already know the theory of relativity. And I'll get to that in just a few moments.

So physics is something that describes the entire physical universe—from the smallest subatomic particles (the quarks and the electrons) to the grand scale of the entire universe, and how it seems to be evolving, and whether it's going to have an ending, and when it had a beginning. All these questions are in the realm of physics. So, it's a great big subject, and it's important to every one, not just physicists.

Physics, as a subject, divides into two very, very broad classes. And these are historically based, and they have names that can be slightly misleading. So I want to make a clarification here about the names. One subject is classical physics; the other is modern physics.

Classical physics is, basically, the physics that was developed before the year 1900. Now, you might say, well that's old-fashioned physics. That's ancient physics. We don't really want to know about that. Well, you're going to need to know a little bit about classical physics to understand how modern physics differs. Furthermore, classical physics—which is what we tend to teach, primarily, in introductory physics courses at the college level, and certainly in high school physics, and any earlier physics we teach—classical physics is very much relevant physics, and it's even very much contemporary physics. You can't do something like design a skyscraper that will stand up, or develop an anti-lock braking system for cars and understand how it works, or build a heart monitor, or an electrocardiograph machine, or engineer an electric power distribution system, or build a compact disc player—many, many, many modern technologies depend very much on classical physics.

So that old-fashioned physics that was developed before the 1900s, so called classical physics, is really very contemporary physics, it's important physics, and it describes many of the things we do today—even launching a spacecraft to Jupiter; or putting satellites in Earth orbit; or sending people to the moon; or any high technology things like that that don't involve subatomic physics, semiconductor electronics, or things like that—they're still in the realm of classical physics. So classical physics is an important branch of physics.

Next comes modern physics. Modern physics was developed in the twentieth century. It arose out of what seemed to be very slight discrepancies between classical physics and the reality of the physical world that were noticed in the second half of the nineteenth century. Those ideas grew into crises in physics—and that's what we'll be exploring in this course—and those crises eventually led to the development of two key ideas in what are called modern physics.

Now, before I go on with that, let me again distinguish: Modern physics does not mean the physics of the last decade or the last few decades. Modern physics has a distinct meaning. It means the key physical ideas that were developed to explain physical reality in the twentieth century. The main ideas were developed early in this century between 1905 and about 1930. We will explore those ideas in great depth in this course, and we will also look a little bit at some of the newer more contemporary ideas, or some of the observations in, say, astrophysics that have been used to verify those early ideas. But this course is primarily about the key ideas of twentieth century physics. The big ideas. The two great big ideas. And what are those big ideas?

Well, the two big ideas are *relativity*—developed primarily by Albert Einstein, although with help from others—and *quantum physics*, which was developed by a whole slew of physicists. Einstein first told us about relativity in 1905. He expanded on relativity in 1914.

And the rest of the twentieth century constituted of an exploration by physicists trying to verify that Einstein was correct. And in the last 10 years, and even in the last five years, we've had some remarkably dramatic confirmations of Einstein's theories, although the essence of those theories was confirmed very early in the century.

What does relativity do? Well, in a nutshell, relativity is a great kind of equalizer. A democratizer. Most people think of relativity and they think of strange things like the time travel twins story I told you earlier. Or they think about $E=mc^2$. And maybe they think about nuclear weapons, which really have nothing to do with relativity. They think about bizarre, esoteric things happening to space and time. That's true. Relativity tells us about bizarre, esoteric things that happen to space and time.

But the essence of relativity is very different. The essence of relativity is that all of us are equal. And we're going to explore and understand how that developed. But in a nutshell, let me just tell you what relativity says. It says your point of view doesn't matter. It says everybody has equal access to the physical laws that govern the way the universe works. And by everybody, I mean it doesn't matter where you are—what planet you're on, whether you're in interstellar space, whether you're in some distant galaxy—physics looks the same to you as it does to me here on Earth. It doesn't matter how you're moving. You could be in an airplane moving at 600 miles an hour and physics acts just the same there. You read a physics textbook. You learn the laws of physics. You do experiments. And they work just the same in that airplane as they do here on Earth. You could be in a spacecraft whizzing by Earth at 90 percent of the speed of light and the laws of physics would still work.

Relativity is in essence a great equalizer. It makes us all equal. It puts all places and all states of motion in the universe on an equal footing. In the process, it leads to these bizarre notions like time travel, like stretching of space, squeezing of time, and so on. It leads to $E=mc^2$ and to the equivalence of matter and energy. But the basic idea of relativity is a simple one. It says we're all equal. It says we all see physics the same. There's no special place. There's no special state of motion. And, in telling you that, I've told you the essence of relativity. You know relativity, once you know that.

In a way, relativity has elaborated on the Copernican revolution—the idea that Earth is no longer the center of the universe. And relativity says there's no special place. Earth is not special as a place, it's not special as a state of motion. And, furthermore, there's no place or state of motion that is special.

The second of the enormous ideas of twentieth century physics—the modern physics ideas—is quantum physics. And quantum physics is a little bit harder to pin down in one basic idea. But if I can try to do it, it's the notion that at the fundamental scales the universe is grainy in a sense. It's built of little discrete parts. It isn't continuously subdividable.

Think about a glass of water. Pour off half of it. You're still left with half a glass of water. Pour off half of that. You're left with a quarter of a glass of water. Pour off half of that. You're left with an eighth. And keep doing that. You've always got liquid water. Will you ever reach a point where you don't have liquid water? Well, at some point in human history that was an open question. Today we know the answer. The answer is that eventually you get down to the point where there's one water molecule in there. One H_2O molecule, consisting of an oxygen atom and two hydrogen atoms. And once you've reached that point, you can't subdivide the water any further. You've got one water molecule. You can take it apart. If you take it apart, you have different entities—oxygen and hydrogen. So the universe is not continuously subdividable. That was known before the twentieth century.

What's new about quantum physics is it quantizes or makes discrete—not only matter, which is broken up into molecules and atoms and subatomic particles—but it also quantizes energy—the other essential stuff of the universe. And as we'll see later, relativity makes matter and energy somewhat interchangeable. So, it's not surprising that this happens.

Quantum physics tells us that the world at the most fundamental level consists of discrete, little bundles of stuff. Bundles of matter. Bundles of energy. It's like buying eggs in the store. You can buy a dozen eggs. You could probably buy a half a dozen eggs. You might even convince the grocer to sell you one egg. But there is no way in the world you're going to buy half an egg or a quarter of an egg. An egg is simply not further subdividable and still have it be an egg. And that's the essence of quantum physics. The universe, including the energy that makes it go, is not infinitely subdividable but comes in discrete little hunks. And although that idea—like the idea of relativity, that no place or motion is special—the idea of quantum physics that the universe is fundamentally discrete, that sounds like a very easy idea to grasp. That egg analogy is a good one. But that leads to very bizarre consequences. For example, the tunneling situation I described. For example, the fact that the, at the fundamental level, the laws that govern the universe are not even deterministic. They don't say, "This will happen if you do this." They say this may happen with a 70 percent chance of this outcome, and a 30 percent chance of this outcome, or whatever. The universe at the fundamental level—this discreteness of matter and energy tells us—is fundamentally statistical. And we have a whole new way of looking at the universe in causality, as a result of that.

So those are the two big ideas of twentieth-century physics. And what this course is about, again, is to expose you to those ideas in a way that makes them understandable to people who have no particular scientific background. Let me give you just the briefest hint of how we're going to do this.

The course is going to be divided into basically two big halves. The first half is going to take us through the *special theory of relativity*. This was the first of the two relativity theories; the one that Einstein developed and published in the year 1905. And it has been very, very highly confirmed by all experiments that have been done since then.

We're going to spend a good deal of time on special relativity. We'll take about four lectures of history. Understanding classical physics. Understanding the contradictions that rose from classical physics. Contradictions that we'll worry about both with relativity and quantum physics.

But after about four lectures, we'll begin to plunge into the essence of special relativity. And we're going to spend through Lecture Twelve on special relativity. And the reason for so much emphasis on this particular subject is special relativity is the most easily understandable of the modern physics ideas. It requires almost no mathematics. And this is a course that's basically devoid of mathematics. So I'm going to present all this material in a non-mathematical way. But if you wanted to understand special relativity thoroughly and mathematically, high school algebra would suffice.

So relativity, special relativity, is an easy to understand subject. I can get you to understand thoroughly and logically why it has to be true.

I can get you to believe in that time travel. I'm not just going to tell you that, I'm going to make you believe that that has to be the case. And you'll understand the full logical progression.

After we do special relativity, we'll spend a few lectures on *general relativity*, which is Einstein's extension of special relativity to cover all states of motion. And it turns out to be a theory of gravity. And it's the theory that predicts the existence of bizarre things like black holes, and wormholes, and white holes and the kind of time travel that occurred in the movie *Contact*. If you've seen that where you go through a wormhole tunnel through space and time. General relativity talks about very strange things like that. It's harder to grasp mathematically. It's harder for me to show you the full, logical flow. We aren't going to spend as much time on it. But, you will get the essence of what general relativity is about.

And then the remaining lectures will be about quantum physics—most of them dealing with, again, the fundamental ideas that were developed by about the year 1930 when people realized just how strange the world, at the subatomic level, was.

And then we'll move on from there and look briefly at some very modern ideas that are outgrowths of quantum mechanics. We'll look at some experiments that have been done in the last few decades that are still causing controversy about the philosophical interpretation of quantum physics—because quantum physics is subject to interpretation, which is still a matter of great philosophical debate. And then, in the very end, we'll look at very contemporary searches for a so-called *theory of everything*—ideas in physics that would be able to explain everything from gravity to the structure of an electron and everything in between with one theory of everything. We aren't there yet, but there are some people who think we're close. And we'll get a glimpse of what those theories are.

Now, I want to say a few more things about physics before I actually plunge into the material. First of all, I want to say that physics is a human activity. I want to remind you that although we're trying to talk here about the content of physics primarily, there's the human touch behind it. And I don't have a lot of time to bring that in, but I will mention it where possible. It's very definitely a human activity. There's been a great deal of controversy in the last few years in fact about just whether physics is another human activity and the laws of physics are like texts we human beings have made up, or whether they reflect some underlying physical reality. I happen to believe, and most of my fellow physicists believe, that the laws of physics, as we describe them, are either fairly accurate reflections or very good approximations of an underlying objective physical reality. We happen to believe that. I think it would be difficult to motivate doing physics if we didn't believe that.

That doesn't mean physics isn't influenced by human characteristics. Relativity probably would have been discovered soon after 1905 by somebody other than Einstein if he hadn't done it. But Einstein's unique genius, perhaps, made it come out sooner. It's also probably true that those subjects we choose to study in physics, those problems we choose to investigate, are influenced by the kinds of people we are. They're influenced by gender. They're influenced by cultural backgrounds. They're influenced by things like that. So, this is not to say that science, although it studies an objective reality, isn't affected by human issues. I think it is. But I think what it ultimately tries to study is something that is underlying, objectively real.

I also want to dispel another notion about science, and physics in particular. There's this notion about the scientific method. And it's actually, I think, enhanced by the way science is taught—not necessarily always as creatively as it might be—in the public schools.

We're given this notion that the scientist is somebody who sort of thinks up a hypothesis, and writes it down very carefully, and then puts on the white lab coat and marches into the lab, and does all kinds of experiments, and either verifies or throws out the hypothesis. It's a very rigid, rigorous process; very carefully spelled out what you do.

Now, some science is done that way. And probably 99 percent of scientists are working in established areas of science where that is an appropriate way to do things. Does this drug kill cancer? I think it does. So I invent an experiment. I say, I'm going to test this drug. I'm going to put it on cancer cells. I'm going to see if they die. I go in the laboratory and I do that. Can I make a smaller computer chip by using this quantum mechanical property of the electron to build this particular device? I think I can. So I make a hypothesis. I put on my lab coat. I go in and I try to build the device and I see if it works. Those are manifestations of the, sort of, basic scientific method as it's taught in schools.

But I think the great science, the big science, the science that takes us leaps ahead in our understanding of physical reality is very different. I think that's a creative activity much more akin to art, or composition of music, or other creative human endeavors than it is to the sort of dry sense people have of science as this dull scientific method kind of thing. Science is a very creative activity, and it's most creative, in particular, when it's taking these big leaps forward.

Einstein didn't do experiments. Einstein thought up relativity in his head. He said this is the way the world has to be. And he wrote it down. And, later, the world proved to be that way when people did experiments. Science is a very creative activity, and I hope in this course you'll get a sense of that. Because we'll see how some of the great minds of modern physics struggled with the bizarre consequences of what they were studying.

So remember that this is a human activity, and I'll try to emphasize that occasionally. But I won't give it as much emphasis as it deserves in a course of this relatively short length for this big a topic.

Now, to end this lecture I want to say one thing, again, to all of you who are sitting there saying, "Well, gee, this is not something I'm going to understand." It is something you're going to understand. My goal and my whole professional goal as a science teacher is to make science, particularly physics, comprehensible to the average person. You need to be intelligent. You need to be open-minded. But you do not need to know anything about science to understand what I am about to describe. It doesn't take an Einstein to understand modern physics. It may have taken an Einstein to come up with modern physics. But once the genius of Einstein had done that, all of us can understand what modern physics has to say. And that's my goal. So, if you're an interested, non-scientist—you gotta be interested—but if you're interested, stay with me and you will understand this material.

And I'm going to end by giving you an example that I think will convince you that you really know a lot more about modern physics than you think. You even know relativity. Let me imagine that you're playing tennis. You're playing tennis on a cruise ship. Now, if you're not into tennis, make it ping-pong, make it soccer, make it just tossing a ball back and forth with someone, tossing a bone to your dog. I don't care what you're doing, but you are doing some kind of activity that involves maybe tossing a ball around. And you're doing it on a cruise ship. And we're going to put you below decks, so there isn't a problem of wind from the motion of the ship. And the ship is moving through calm water, and it's moving at a steady rate of speed. It's not turning. The water is not rocking it. There aren't big waves. It's just plowing steadily along. Now, since you know how to play tennis, I assert that you already know a lot about the laws of physics in your muscles. You know what a ball is going to do when it's hit with the racquet—where it's going to move. Your muscles can judge the laws of physics that describe the motion of that ball. And that is what makes you a decent tennis player. So you know the laws of physics in your muscles even if you think you don't know them in your brain.

So now you go below decks into this enclosed tennis court. The ship is plowing along through the water at 40 miles an hour or something, and you proceed to play tennis. Let me ask you some questions. Does it matter to you whether you're the tennis player that's facing the forward direction of the ship or the backward direction of the ship? Does it matter that the ship is moving? Do you have to say to yourself, "Gee, I'm facing the forward direction. The ship's moving 50 miles an hour, I gotta take that in to account when I swing?" Of course not. Does the ship's motion make any difference to you? Of course not. You play tennis on that steadily moving cruise ship exactly like you would back home on solid Earth. Makes no difference at all. If it did, you'd have a real problem. Because when you sat on an airplane, for example, and tried to eat the little peanuts they bring you, you'd have to worry about the fact that those peanuts are going 600 miles an hour with the airplane. How am I going to get them to my mouth? That doesn't matter. And it doesn't matter playing tennis on the cruise ship.

Now, you're done playing tennis, and you want a nice hot cup of tea afterwards. If you're not a tea drinker, have coffee. But it's got to be instant because I want you to put it in the microwave to heat the water. Do you think that when you push the start button on the microwave you've got to worry, "Oh, wait a minute, the microwaves in this oven are going to be upset by the fact that the ship is moving this way at 50 miles an hour. I gotta worry about that. I gotta set the time differently. Maybe I gotta turn the microwave oven. Maybe I gotta do something strange." Do you worry about that? Of course not. You stick the teacup in the microwave oven. You press three minutes. And your tea water gets hot. Doesn't make any difference about the motion of the ship.

Now, I really want you to believe that. And it's very obvious. If that isn't obvious, let me give you two other examples that, I think, will make it even more obvious. The last of which is really only possible to understand in the contemporary era.

For the second one, let's imagine we now, have a base on Venus. Not hard to imagine—30, 50 years from now. And you're in the recreational room of that base on Venus. You're stationed there as one of the scientists working away or something, or maybe you're one of the maintenance people, or maybe you're one of the cooks. You're doing anything there. But you're going to go play some tennis in the recreation hall. And the recreation hall consists of a big inflated dome, like you've seen some tennis courts in. And inside it is an atmosphere exactly like the Earth's, because Venus's atmosphere—with a super runaway greenhouse effect like we hope we don't get on Earth—is way too hot and thick and so on to nurture us or to play tennis in. So inside this dome is an Earth-type atmosphere. And Venus's gravity is essentially the same as Earth's. So you go in this thing, and you play tennis.

Does it matter to you that you're on Venus? Nope. The tennis works just as it would on Earth. Gravity is the same. The air is the same. The tennis ball obeys the same laws of physics. Works just the same. However, you're on Venus, tens of millions of miles from Earth. And, depending on where and when Earth and Venus are in their orbits, they may be moving, relative to each other, at speeds of 20, 30, 40, 50 miles per second. Do you have to sit in that tennis court in Venus and say to yourself, "Gee, I'm moving at 45 miles a second relative to Earth. It's a lot faster than I can hit a tennis ball." Do I have to worry about that fact, in order to play this game? Well, of course you don't. The tennis ball, and Venus, doesn't care what Earth is doing. There's nothing special about Earth. Physics works the same on Venus as it does on Earth.

And then you get done with your tennis game on Venus, and you step over to the microwave oven to heat your tea. You put it in the microwave oven. You say to yourself, "Gee, Venus. Forty-five miles a second relative to Earth. It's going to do something strange to the microwave oven. Maybe it won't even work. Maybe the microwaves will get left behind and they won't heat my tea." Nonsense. You press the start button, you go for three minutes, and you have boiling water. Works just the same as on Earth.

Now, the last example is not one I could have given you in the earlier part of the century when people were first discovering modern physics. But now I can. Because now we know through astronomical observations, particularly recent ones with the Hubble space telescope, that there are objects so distant from us, and I'll explain later in the course why distance matters here, so distant from us that they are moving away from us at speeds of 80 percent or more of the speed of light. That's fast. The speed of light is about 200,000 miles a second. So these things are moving away from us at maybe 160,000 miles a second.

These are galaxies. We don't see them as galaxies when we look at them in space, because we're seeing light from a long, long time ago. But now they've presumably evolved into galaxies. Maybe some of them have stars around them like the sun. And maybe some of those have Earth-like planets around them.

So imagine there's yourself or some other creature on an Earth-like planet around a star in a distant galaxy that's moving away from Earth at 80 percent of the speed of light. And you're going to play tennis there. And you get out your tennis balls. And do you say to yourself, "Gee, Earth, 12 billion light years away, matters a lot, and I've got to figure out the fact that I'm going at 80 percent of the speed of light relative to Earth in order to play this tennis, right?" Nonsense. The laws of physics are the same for everybody, and you sit there on that distant planet and you play tennis just like you would normally. And then you pop over to the microwave oven. And you put your teacup in. And you press the button. And you don't worry about the fact that the microwaves, which move at the speed of light, are in an oven, which itself is being whisked along, relative to Earth, at 80 percent of the speed of light.

Why don't you worry about that? Because it all makes sense to us that the physics that happens, the laws that govern the way the physical world works, should be the same for everybody.

Does that idea make sense to you? It should. Ask yourself, if you think it doesn't make sense, are you some kind of closet Aristotelian who believes the Earth is the center of everything. Well, if you don't believe the Earth is the center of everything and the only special place in the universe, it follows pretty logically that the laws of physics ought to be the same for everybody, and that your motion, relative to Earth, ought not to matter.

If you believe that—and I assert that you ought to believe that if you accept these examples I've just given you—if you believe that, then you already believe in your gut and in your brain the essence of Einstein's relativity. Because the essence of Einstein's relativity is that Earth is not a special place and Earth's state of motion is not a special state of motion. And anyone out there anywhere in the universe who chooses to do physics experiments—playing tennis is a physics experiment because it's an experiment with the laws of nature and how they act on the tennis ball; and heating tea in a microwave oven is a physics experiment because it's an experiment in that case about the laws of electromagnetism, which are behind the operation of a microwave oven and how they behave. And if you choose to do those physics experiments, no matter where you choose to do them, they will come out the same.

Now at this point you could shut off the tape and walk away and tell all your friends, "I know all there is to know about relativity," because in essence you do.

Relativity is simply the statement that the laws of physics are the same for everybody. Why is it so hard to understand? Because it has implications that are not obvious and not easy to grasp and seem to run counter to common sense. And so it's going to take a while to explore those notions and understand them. It's also going to take a while to understand how humankind came to the idea that the laws of physical reality are the same for everyone. That's what our task is in the lectures to come. But as we end this one, let me remind you that you do, in fact, already know and believe the essence of the theory of relativity—that everybody has the same laws of physics, that the universe behaves the same way for everyone.

Lecture Two

Heaven and Earth, Place and Motion

Scope:

Understanding motion is the key to understanding space and time, because to move is to move through *space* and *time*. Is there a "natural" state of motion? To the ancients, there were two different "yes" answers: In the perfect realm of the heavens, objects naturally moved in perfect circles. On Earth, however, the natural state was to be at rest, as close as possible to the center of the Earth—the center of the ancients' universe. Copernicus's Sun-centered universe deprived Earth of its special place, but retained perfect circles. Kepler found that the heavenly motions were not perfect circles, but ellipses. Peering through his telescope, Galileo discovered further evidence of celestial imperfection. At the same time, he laid the foundation for a more modern understanding of motion and gravity.

Outline

I. A brief history of physics before Newton.

    A. We concentrate on *motion*. Why? Because to move is to move through *space* and *time*. The natures of space and time are intimately tied with motion.

    B. A useful question is the following: Is there a natural state of motion?

    C. The ancients thought that there were different "natural states" for terrestrial and celestial motion.

        1. Aristotle (c. 349 BC) described a geocentric universe with planets and Sun orbiting Earth in perfect circles Ptolemy (c. 140 AD) added circles-on-circles ("epicycles") to represent planetary motion more accurately Terrestrial objects naturally assume a state of rest close to the center of the universe (Earth); force is required to maintain motion.

        2. Copernicus (1543) posited a Sun-centered universe, but maintained the celestial/terrestrial distinction and perfect circular motion in the celestial realm.

3. Kepler (c. 1610), through careful study of planetary observations collected by Tycho Brahe (1546–1601) showed that planetary orbits are ellipses, not circles. He developed mathematical laws describing the orbits, but gave no explanation for why the planets moved as they did.

4. Galileo (1564–1642) discovered that the Sun was blemished with sunspots, found moons orbiting Jupiter, and observed the phases of Venus. These discoveries helped dispel the notion of celestial perfection and lent support to Copernicus's heliocentric theory.

5. Experimenting with motion on Earth, Galileo concluded that all objects fall with the same acceleration. Through a "thought experiment," he developed the law of inertia—that an object continues in straight-line motion at constant speed unless disturbed by an outside influence (force). Thus, he redefined the "natural state" of motion as straight-line motion at constant speed. According to Galileo, force is needed for *change* in motion, not for motion itself.

Essential Reading:

Mook and Vargish, *Inside Relativity*, Chapter 1, Sections 1–5.

Hoffmann, *Relativity and Its Roots*, Chapter 2 (here and elsewhere in Hoffmann, skip the boldfaced material unless you want more math background than is needed for this course).

Suggested Reading:

Einstein and Infeld, *The Evolution of Physics*, Chapter 1, through p. 33.

Questions to Consider:

1. For the ancients, objects in the heavens moved naturally in circular motion. Would Galileo consider circular motion a "natural state" of motion? Why or why not?

2. Why isn't Galileo's conclusion that objects naturally move in straight-line motion at constant speed obvious from our everyday experience? Can you describe an environment in which it would be obvious?

Lecture Two—Transcript
Heaven and Earth, Place and Motion

Welcome to Lecture Two: "Heaven and Earth, Place and Motion." I advertise this is a course about modern physics, but in the first lecture I also talked at some length about classical physics as a way of contrasting the physics before the year 1900 with the modern physics that this course is primarily about.

In this lecture I've got to take you back even further to what I'll call ancient physics. Pre-classical physics. Physics before the time of Isaac Newton. Because we want to understand how ideas evolve from that physics into classical physics and then set the stage for the several quandaries I mentioned that then led to the introduction of modern physics.

I'm going to concentrate in this lecture and in subsequent lectures for a while on the question of motion. Now, this sounds like kind of a dull, dry topic. And many students going through introductory physics courses, unfortunately, come away thinking, "Gee. Motion. Why do I really care about that?" Well, if you think for a minute about motion, you'll realize it's the key to everything that happens. If there were no motion everything would stop. There would be no change. There would be no time. You wouldn't get from one place to another. Electrons wouldn't jump across the synapses in your nerves, in your brain, and you wouldn't think. There'd be nothing happening. Motion is what makes everything happen.

Why are we going to concentrate on motion? Now, one reason physicists concentrate on motion is because they'd like to predict how things are going to move. If I launch this rocket with this velocity, will I get it into orbit around Venus? for example, is a question. If I slam on the brakes with this much force, will my motion stop in time to avoid hitting the car in front of me? How does the electron move in this complicated new molecule I've synthesized that may be a drug that cures cancer or whatever. These are questions about motion.

We need to understand motion to understand how the world works. But, that's not the reason in this course for our being interested in motion. The reason we are interested in motion here is because what does it mean to move? It means to move from place to place. That is, through space. And it takes time to move. There is no such thing, we don't think, as instantaneous motion. Being here and then, instantaneously being here. So, motion is inextricably tied with the key ideas of space and time.

And space and time, if you think about them, are the fabric of physical reality—the underlying stage in which all physical events take place. So, if we understand motion, we have a clue to the nature of space and time. And it's no secret, as you understand from the first lecture with the time traveling twins, it's no secret that relativity does strange things to our common sense notions of space and time. So we've got to understand how those common sense notions were developed. And then we've got to understand what a true understanding of motion tells us about the real nature of space and time. So we're going to be emphasizing questions of motion.

And we're going to ask a useful question. And I ask you to keep this question in mind throughout at least the first two-thirds of the course, because it's going to pop up again, and again, and again. And the question is this: Is there a natural state of motion? Is there some way things sort of left to their own devices like to move—or maybe not move? Is there a natural state of motion? If there is a natural state of motion, what is it? If there isn't a natural state of motion, does everything just want to stop? You might have thought that was the natural state. But, think again. Things don't just stop. Electrons are whizzing around. Cars are moving. The air is moving. The planets are going around the sun. Maybe being at rest is not such a natural state. We'll come to understand that.

To answer the question, is there a natural state of motion, as we now understand the answer, we've got to go back though and look at what the answers were in ancient times and then in classical physics times. And so that's what I intend to do. And in this lecture I want to look particularly at the ancient's answer. And the ancient's answer is interesting because it's a blend of science and philosophy and theology.

In ancient times, the universe was divided into two realms. There was the earthly realm. That was the realm of the base, the imperfect, the crude, the solid, the material stuff—like us, and rocks, and water, and oceans—the Earth. And there was one set of rules that governed how things happened on Earth.

And then there were the heavens. Hence my title, "Heaven and Earth, Place and Motion." There were two places—the heavens and the Earth—and they had different laws of physics. If you want to think about these ancient ideas as laws of physics.

And the answer to the question, what's the natural state of motion, had a different answer on Earth and a different answer in the heavens. And the answer given for Earth was very simple. The natural state of motion for earthly entities is to be as close as possible to the center of the Earth—which was the center of the universe. And the Earth was a realm, again, of the material, and the base, and the solid, and so on.

And so that explains a lot of things. It explains the fact that if I take this ball, for example, and drop it, after a while it ends up at rest as close as it can possibly get to the center of the Earth—which happens to be the floor in this instance. So, the philosophical sense that things on Earth tended toward the center of the Earth and to come to a state of rest as close to the center of the Earth as possible seems to be born out by experiments. Again, dropping a ball is a physics experiment. I'm challenging physical reality to tell me how it behaves, and I'm learning something about it. That experiment seems to verify the ancient notion that motion on Earth ultimately has a natural state, which is to be at rest as close as possible to the center of the Earth.

Notice that that is also, in a sense, a philosophical explanation for the phenomenon that we now call gravity, because it sort of gives a teleological, a purposeful, a philosophical explanation for why that tennis ball ended up on the floor. It wants to be as close as possible to the center of the Earth and to be at rest—and it got into that state.

So the answer, what's the natural state of motion, to the ancients for objects on Earth was they want to be as close as possible to the center of the Earth and they want to be at rest. And that is easy and done with and explains a lot of physical phenomena that we observe.

In the heavenly realm, on the other hand, things were very different. The heavens are the realm of the ethereal, the spiritual, the stars, the planets. People really didn't know what they were. They were things up there in the heavens. And there there's a very different, natural state of motion. The natural state of motion of the heavens, according to the ancients, is circular motion. Move in a perfect circle. A circle is about the most perfect geometrical form you can think of. It has no corners. It has no beginning or end. It's everywhere the same. It's a beautiful, perfect thing. And the idea was motion in the heavens was circular motion. And objects in the heavens simply continued in circular motion. That was the natural thing for them to do.

There were various theories about why that happened. There were also various theories to explain funny phenomena of earthly motion. For example, if I throw a ball, it keeps moving for a while before it ends up in that natural state. Well, there were theories about air rushing from the front to behind to keep it moving and things like that. But the basic idea was it wanted to end up in that state of rest, whereas objects in the heavens wanted to be moving in those perfect circles just continually.

I want to emphasize one other aspect of this. Why do things move? That's another question we can ask. Well, we've just given a kind of philosophical explanation. Things on Earth move toward the center of the Earth because they'd like to be at rest as close as possible to the center of the Earth. If they're not in that state, according to the ancients, it takes some kind of push to get them going or to keep them going. If you see an object that's moving, for example, an ox cart is moving down the road, the ox is pulling it. That's what makes it move. If the ox stops, it stops moving. If you take your foot off the gas pedal of your car, the car comes to a stop. Albeit, not instantaneously. But sooner or later it ends up in a stopped state. So the idea was you needed to have some kind of push, in that case the push of the tires against the road, ultimately driven by the engine of the car.

You needed to have some kind of push to keep something moving. Absent that push, the thing stops moving. So a fundamental idea of the ancient view of motion is that it takes a push to keep something moving. At least in the terrestrial realm. In the heavenly realm, you have this different situation with the perfect circles and they just continue.

Let's look for a minute more at the heavenly realm. Out of that idea came a sort of cosmology. A picture of what the universe looked like. And let's take a look at the first visual here. This is the picture of the universe as the philosopher Aristotle envisioned it. Aristotle is working in the 300s B.C. and he has a vision of a universe in which the Earth is sitting at the center.

The Earth is surrounded by concentric rings that hold the different planets that are thought to go around the Earth and that also hold the sun, which is also thought to go around the Earth. And farthest out are the so-called fixed stars that stay in the same relative position in the sky, and they are thought to move as one giant sphere around the Earth.

By the way, for those of you who are "watching" this course on audio, I do have a number of visuals. And I've selected the most important ones and put them in the booklet. So I urge you to refer to those. If you're driving your car, you might want to wait until you come to a stoplight or something. But this course is definitely aimed at you audio people as well. And when I describe a visual that isn't in the book, and this is an example, I'll just tell you what we're looking at. So we're looking at this picture of the Earth at the center of the universe surrounded by concentric rings holding planets, and in one case the sun.

Well, there is a problem with this picture. One of the things we'd really like our laws of physics and our cosmologies and descriptions of the physical universe to do is correspond to reality. And, unfortunately, the picture Aristotle described of objects going around the Earth doesn't quite make it. And the reason is if you look at the motion of the planets in the sky, they do not seem to describe perfect circles around the Earth. The sun, essentially, does; the distant stars essentially do; but the planets don't. They do strange things.

If you watch a planet, Mars say, or Jupiter, night after night, you'll see it changing its position in the sky relative to the fixed stars. For a while, looking like it's going in a nice circular path around Earth. But then it will pause and it will go backwards for a while—in a little loop. And then it will pick up and go forward again. It isn't describing perfect circular motion around the Earth.

But Aristotle and the other ancients were hung up on the notion that celestial motion must be perfect circles. So it was up to Ptolemy, in about 140 A.D., to come along and modify the Aristotelian picture. And here is what Ptolemy did. He simply took the planets and instead of having the planets moving in perfect circles around the Earth, they moved in little tiny circles—they were called epicycles— around other perfect circles that themselves went around the Earth.

So Ptolemy made a cosmology, a picture of the universe that fit physical reality better. If you study how this system works in which planets are going around the Earth, but then they're also moving in little circles around your path, you'll find that they do in that situation pretty much what they appear to do in the sky. That is, they exhibit this occasional backwards or retrograde motion. And this could be embellished with additional circles upon circles to make it more accurate, and so on.

But the point here is we are emphasizing the notion of perfect circles in the celestial realm. So the universe, according to Ptolemy, is basically like that according to Aristotle. But the circular motions consist not of a single circle around the Earth but circles upon circles. We don't need that for the sun, which appears still to describe a perfect circle.

So that's the picture, according to Ptolemy. And that picture reigned for a couple thousand years. Basically, until Copernicus, in 1543, published the heretical idea that no, the Earth is not the center of the universe. Instead, thought Copernicus, the sun is the center of the universe.

And this is the great Copernican revolution. And it's the first step in what is ultimately going to lead us to Einstein's general theory of relativity. It's the first step in saying Earth is not a special place, and Earth's motion is not a special state of motion.

Copernicus emphasized the business of place. I'm going emphasize also the business of motion, because that's what's tied up with relativity. So what does the universe, according to Copernicus, look like? Well, Copernicus was loath to give up the perfect circles upon circles. So his cosmology also had a sun at the center, it was surrounded by orbits of planets, and a circular orbit of the Earth, and the planetary orbits needed to have circles upon circles, because they didn't seem to be describing even quite perfect circles around the sun. And Copernicus was really insistent on maintaining this view that the celestial motions are perfect. So he came up with a cosmology—again, circles upon circles. But here the sun is at the center.

Well, the next bold step was taken by Kepler, who was working in 1610 roughly, and he was working with data that had been collected painstakingly by the astronomer Tycho Brahe. And Tycho had amassed years and years and years of data on the positions of the planets. And, on the basis of that data, Kepler concluded something quite different. He concluded that motion in the heavens, the motion of the planets around the sun, at least, were not perfect circles, but they were ellipses. And I'm showing here a picture of an ellipse, for you audio people it's simply an egg shaped curve with the sun not at the center, but off at a place called the focus, which is at one side.

This is a highly exaggerated picture. The orbits of the planets are not very elliptical at all. They are almost perfectly circular. The Earth's, for instance, differs from perfect circularity by about three percent. If I were to draw it, you'd have a hard time distinguishing it from a perfect circle. So this is highly exaggerated. Orbits of comets do look exaggerated like this. So do orbits of the satellites that are used to provide television service to Siberia, for example. They describe great looping orbits that take them hanging for a long time over the extremes of the Northern Hemisphere. And then they whiz down around in these elliptical orbits.

So elliptical orbits do happen, but they aren't the orbits that the planets follow. The orbits the planets follow are circular, almost. But they are measurably different. And Kepler said they are ellipses not circles, and not only did he say that, he made up laws that describe how fast the planets were moving at different parts of the ellipse in relation to the period—the time it takes to go around—and the size of the elliptical orbit.

So he described mathematically what these orbits looked like and how the planets moved in the orbits. But he gave us no physical explanation. He didn't say, "Why do they move in these orbits?" He just said, "I think they do."

So, where have we moved? We've moved away from the notion of an Earth-centered universe. That was Copernicus's big step. We now have a sun-centered universe, but in Copernicus's idea still with perfect circles.

Now we've moved away from that further to a universe in which the orbits of the planets appear to be ellipses not circles. And Kepler is telling us how to describe mathematically what those elliptical orbits are. But we have no explanation for why the ellipses are there. And we still have this dichotomy between motion on Earth and motion in the heavens.

And now we move to someone who is probably the most important figure in all of science. And that's Galileo Galilee. Galileo, who lived from 1564 to 1642, was a real experimentalist. People like Kepler were looking at observational data. Galileo also got his hands on real things. He purportedly dropped objects off the Leaning Tower of Pisa. Whether that's true or not, he certainly did experiment with terrestrial motion on Earth and tried to come up with an explanation and an understanding of how that motion behaved. He tried to answer the question—and succeeded in answering the question—what's the natural state of motion on Earth.

Galileo did several things. We'll talk a little more later about his experiments with earthly motion. But he also did some observational astronomy. And he developed the first astronomical telescope. He was alive at the era when the whole idea of lenses for eyeglasses, on vision correction, had just been invented. And he made a telescope, and he pointed it heavenward. And he saw some things that had never been seen before.

I just want to describe for you three things Galileo saw, because they shook the foundations of this philosophical idea that the heavens up there were somehow perfect and different from the base and coarse and crude Earth down here. The first thing Galileo saw, I don't know if it was the first thing temporally, but one thing he saw when he looked at Jupiter—and you can do this observation with a pair of binoculars—if you look at Jupiter, you'll see what Galileo saw. He saw four little dots lined up in a line on either side of Jupiter. You look on different nights—they're in different places. Sometimes you can't see one or two of them because they are behind or in front of Jupiter. But if you watch Jupiter, when it's up in the sky at night, on different nights, you'll see these little dots that are in line right across Jupiter's equator, on either side of Jupiter. Those are the so-called Galilean satellites of Jupiter. They are clearly, and were clearly to Galileo, a kind of miniature solar system. They represented moons of Jupiter, going around Jupiter in the same way the Earth's moon goes around the Earth.

And so, Galileo had, for the first time, an example of another solar system–like thing, another miniature cosmology. And it clearly had Jupiter at the center and the moons going around it. And that helped confirm the notion that there was nothing so special or unusual about the Earth—being sort of like a moon of the sun going around the sun along with all the other planets.

By discovering another miniature solar system, if you will, Galileo had confirmed the Copernican idea that the sun was a solar system with the sun at the center and the planets going around it. Galileo's discovery of Jupiter's moons, I think, is a little bit like what will happen when eventually perhaps we discover life somewhere else in the universe. We'll have a second example. All of a sudden what happened here on Earth, that many scientists don't think is unique, will be proved not to be unique. Similarly, Galileo discovered the moons going around Jupiter, and for the first time the solar system idea was not unique. It was a commonplace or, not commonplace, but at least it was a physical occurrence that had occurred more than once. So that was an important observation.

The second observation Galileo made was of the phases of Venus. You're all aware of the phases of the moon. Sometimes it's full. Sometimes it's a new moon, and you can't see it. Sometimes it's a crescent. Sometimes it's a half moon. Sometimes it's gibbous—not quite full—and so on.

Why does the moon have phases? Because the moon goes around the Earth, and at different times in its orbit it's in a different place in relation to the sun. For instance, when it's a full moon, you'll notice the full moon rises at sunset. Why? Because the sun is on one side of the Earth. The moon is on the other side. And it is getting full sunlight. That's why the full moon always rises at sunset. And always sets at sunrise, for example. At other phases, the moon is being lit—only part of it is being illuminated. Only the part of it you can see from Earth is being illuminated. And we get the phases. In the moon's case, although the moon goes through different phases, the phases are always the same size.

Galileo observed the phases of Venus. Venus goes through full and crescent, and so on. But there's something else that happens with the phases of Venus. When Venus is full, it's a very small circle. When Venus is a crescent, it's much larger. Why would that be?

Well, there's an easy explanation for that in terms of the Copernican picture. In the Copernican picture, Venus is full when it's on the opposite side of the sun from the Earth, and therefore, it's farthest away, and therefore, it looks smaller. It's a crescent when it's relatively near the same side of the sun as the Earth is. The Earth is only seeing a small sliver of the lit up part of Venus. And, therefore, we see a crescent. And it looks much bigger because Venus is much closer.

It would be very difficult to explain that observation in terms of the Aristotelian, Ptolemaic idea that the Earth is at the center of the universe. Because there Venus is going around the Earth. And, except for that little circle on a circle, there's very little change in its distance from Earth. So, the observation of the phases of Venus was a very important one in helping to verify the Copernican notion, again, that the Earth is not special. The Earth is not the center of everything. We're moving away from Earth-centeredness with that observation.

The final observation that Galileo made is that he looked at the sun and he observed sunspots. Timing here, by the way, is remarkably lucky because the sun, very soon after Galileo's time, went into a phase called the Maunder Minimum that we solar physicists, and I happen to be a solar physicist in my research field, we don't understand why that occurred, but the sun went through a period when it had almost no sunspots for a long time.

What are sunspots? Well, to Galileo they were dark blemishes on the surface of the sun. He hadn't actually discovered sunspots. The ancient Chinese had discovered them much earlier and called them crows and didn't know what they were. And Galileo didn't know either. But the important philosophical point was they were blemishes on the surface of the sun. Here's this celestial body, and it's no longer perfect. And, by the way, you look at the moon and you see it has craters and mountains. It's not perfect either.

Here's a break in the notion that the celestial realm is somehow perfect and somehow distinct from the terrestrial realm. All of a sudden, there are mountains and craters and there are spots on the sun. And it's not perfect up there either. So why should it obey some kind of different, perfect laws?

Galileo didn't get any further than that. But he established the imperfection of the heavens, if you will. And that was a break in this notion of a separate terrestrial and celestial realm.

Then Galileo turned to motion on Earth. And he did several important experiments. The experiment we are most famous with, the experiment in which he supposedly dropped objects off the Leaning Tower of Pisa. That was an experiment, which, if it occurred, verified the notion that all objects fall toward the Earth with the same, not speed, but acceleration. They gain speed at exactly the same rate. It's a difficult experiment to do accurately. Air resistance gets in the way. But Galileo, if he did it from the Tower of Pisa, was able, by dropping objects of different weight, to confirm that. They didn't fall at grossly different rates. That was an important understanding of gravity.

Then Galileo carried out an important "thought experiment", which I will describe here and show you in a visual. What Galileo did was to imagine a ball rolling in some kind of trough. The ball starts at some height in the trough. It rolls down to the bottom of the trough. And then it rolls up to the other side. And how far up would it get? Galileo asked. Well, he reasoned that if there were no friction and no air resistance and so on—everything were perfect—the ball would roll to the same height it started out at. And, absent any friction or air resistance, it would simply roll back and forth in that trough continuously. Back and forth. Always rising to the same height. Of course, it doesn't. It eventually slows down because of friction and stops at the bottom.

But, that was Galileo's thought. So, if he rolled a ball from one side of the trough, it will rise to the same height on the other side. What if we make the other side of the trough somewhat longer? What if we take this trough, which is now symmetrical, and we stretch out one side of it? Well, the ball will still rise to the same height, reasons Galileo, in this so-called "thought experiment." He didn't actually do this. But he said what will happen if we did this. It will rise to the same height, vertically. But it has to roll further horizontally to get there because the trough that was originally symmetric is now longer on one side—the side it's going to rise up to—after it rolls down.

And then, said Galileo, "What if we go one step further?" What if we take that trough and lower it completely—make it horizontal at the bottom. So the ball rolls down the trough and then it rolls continually horizontally along the bottom of the track. What happens? Galileo said absent friction and air resistance, it never stops.

Now, the historians of science will tell me I'm being a little bit simplistic here. And I am. Galileo was worried about the curvature of the Earth and other things like that. But, in principle, this is the essence of his idea. Galileo said if this trough never goes back up again, the ball will just continue rolling horizontally without its speed changing. And he reasoned that from this idea of taking the trough and gradually lowering the one side, the ball rolls farther and farther horizontally while rising to the same height. Finally, if it can't ever rise to the same height it started at, it will just continue to go horizontally forever.

And Galileo, therefore, concluded something very, very different about terrestrial motion. He reasoned this way. He said, "Look, if an object is moving at a constant speed in a straight line, what's it going to do? It's going to keep doing that. It's going to move forever in a straight line at constant speed. It's never going to stop."

That idea is crucial to classical physics, and to modern physics as well. That idea is one of the key ideas in understanding motion. What Galileo is saying is: The natural state of motion is not to be at rest on the surface of the Earth. That's a state of motion you get to because of things like friction and air resistance and things that you bump into, like the floor when the ball falls. The natural state of motion is to move in a straight line at constant speed.

It doesn't take a push to have something be moving. This is a crucial point. This is one we teachers of introductory physics spend a lot of time trying to get our students really to believe. It's really true folks. It doesn't take any push to make something move. If you see something moving, the question is not why does it keep moving. The question might be, how did it get moving in the first place? Or, if you see something that's stopped, how did it get stopped if it was earlier moving? The question is not, what keeps it moving? Because it takes no push. No pull. What physicists call a force. It takes no force to keep something moving. That's what Galileo says. And that's what appears to be a correct description of the way motion works.

The natural state of motion is to be moving uniformly in a straight line. And there is a name for that statement. It's a name attributed to both Galileo and Newton. It's called the law of inertia. It says that an object has an inertia. A natural tendency to keep moving. If I take this big ball over here, and I set it into motion, it keeps moving. And it would fall on the floor and crush itself if I didn't stop it. That's because of its inertia. It takes a push to get it started moving. And it takes a push or a pull to stop it. But what it naturally wants to do is move in a straight line at constant speed.

That's the natural state of motion. That's the law of inertia. By virtue of having mass, by being heavy, by having, if you will, weight, although those terms are not quite synonymous, this object, once moving, will keep moving. It takes a push to get it moving. It takes a push to stop it moving. It also takes a push to change the direction of its motion. The motion that is natural, according to Galileo, is uniform motion. That means motion in a straight line at constant speed. If you see any deviation from that, if you see an object speed up or slow down or, and this is the point our introductory physics students sometimes have trouble with, or change its direction, in all those cases you can assume that a force—a push or pull—has acted on it. But if you see it moving in a straight line at constant speed, there is no reason to explain that. That is what it naturally wants to do. Nobody is pushing it or pulling it.

Why is that such a hard idea for us to grasp? Because in most of our world, the experience—push this tennis ball, you see it slowing down. Eventually it stops. Take your foot off the gas of the car again. It ought to just keep rolling forever if what I've just said is true. Well, it is true except there are pushes and pulls working on the car. There's the push of the air against it. There's the friction pushing against the tires. In the case of the ball, there's friction with the table. And again, there's the air pushing back on it. We don't see those forces. They don't manifest themselves the way my hand does as a forcible push or pull. But they're there, and they cause the motion to change.

If we could abstract those forces away, and that's what Galileo's thoughts-on-motion thought experiment did. Or, if we could go to a physical situation like, say, an ice hockey rink. Look at the hockey puck. It whizzes across the ice. There's almost no friction. It would go much further than the size of the ice rink before it slowed down appreciably. Look at the skaters themselves. Unless they dig their skates into the ice to try to force themselves to turn or to start or stop, they simply coast at essentially constant speed. The forces of friction and air resistance, in that case, are small. The pushes and pulls and the natural state of motion reveals itself.

But the reason we have trouble teaching this to introductory physics students and getting them to believe it—it actually makes the world much simpler—and the reason we have such trouble accepting it in our everyday lives is we're all sort of closet Aristotelians, in a sense. I use that term with my students. I tell them they are closet Aristotelians. They sort of believe really in their gut that Aristotle was right. That it takes a push or a pull to make motion, that the natural state of motion is to be at rest on the surface of the Earth. It's not true. The natural state of motion is to move in a straight line at constant speed.

Perhaps the very best example of this I can give you is the Pioneer and Voyager spacecraft, which are now beyond the outer most reaches of the solar system. And they've been going for something close now to 30 years—20 to 30 years. And they are just moving in almost straight lines. There are some slight pushes and pulls from the gravity of the sun and the planets. But they are essentially moving in straight lines at constant speeds. They have no rocket motors going. There's no fuel involved. They're still broadcasting back to us with the radio transmitters, though. And they're way out there. And they're just going to move forever until something pushes or pulls on them—like the pull of a distant star or an alien hand reaching out and grabbing them and trying to figure out where they came from. Otherwise, straight line, constant speed. It's the natural state of motion. It takes no effort. It takes no force. It takes no push or pull.

This is the essential change that Galileo has made. He's developed the law of inertia. He said the natural state of motion is straight-line motion at constant speed. Pushes and pulls are required only for changes in motion. We are going to make a great deal of those two points. If you see a change in motion, you know a push or a pull has occurred. If there is not change in motion, that's perfectly natural. There is no push or pull involved. The law of inertia holds. An object moves in a straight line at constant speed unless a push or a pull acts on it. And out of that is going to come a whole host of classical physics. And that's ultimately going to lead us to the questions that will bring us to relativity.

Lecture Three
The Clockwork Universe

Scope:

Isaac Newton was born in 1642, the year of Galileo's death. Newton developed his famous three laws of motion, quantifying Galileo's earlier idea that uniform, straight-line motion is natural and changes only if outside influences (forces) act. Newton also considered gravity and had the brilliant insight that the same force that pulls an apple to Earth is also what holds the moon in its orbit—thus, putting to rest the false dichotomy between celestial and terrestrial motion. Newton developed the concept of *universal gravitation*, suggesting that every object in the universe attracts every other object, with a force that depends on their masses and the distance between them. Together, Newton's laws of motion and gravity showed that the planets must move in Kepler's elliptical orbits and hinted at the possibility of artificial satellites. The predictability inherent in Newton's laws suggests a "clockwork universe" in which all that happens in the universe is completely determined by the initial motions of its constituents.

Inherent in the ideas of Galileo and Newton is the *Principle of Galilean Relativity*: that the laws of motion work exactly the same way for anyone as long as he or she is moving uniformly. In other words, the laws of physics known to Galileo and Newton preclude such statements as "I am moving" or "I am at rest" from having any absolute meaning.

Outline

I. Newton and his laws.

    A. The personal touch: Newton, the "genius of Cambridge," was born in 1642 (the year Galileo died). He did some of his most productive work while away from Cambridge to escape the plague. Today, Stephen Hawking occupies Newton's chair at Cambridge.

    B. Laws of motion: Newton stated three laws of motion that, in principle, make all motion predictable once the forces acting on objects are known. Thus, the physical universe became completely deterministic, like a vast clockwork.

1. Newton's first law restates Galileo's discovery that objects move uniformly unless acted on by outside forces.
2. Newton's second law, *F=ma*, tells quantitatively how a given force (*F*) produces changes in motion (acceleration, *a*) in an object of mass *m*.
3. Newton's third law, "for every action there is an equal and opposite reaction" says that forces always come in pairs; if object A exerts a force on object B, then B exerts a force of equal strength back on A.

C. Newton's law of gravity.
 1. The famous story of Newton and the apple may be a myth. But if it is true, its significance lies in Newton's realization that apple and moon are attracted toward Earth by the same force, which Newton named *gravity*.
 2. Thus, Newton subsumed celestial and terrestrial motion under the same laws. He generalized to the idea of *universal gravitation*: that every object in the universe attracts every other, with a force that depends on their masses and the distance between them.
 3. Using his law of gravity and his newly invented calculus, Newton proved that the planets must move in elliptical orbits, just as Kepler had observed.
 4. Newton anticipated artificial satellites, showing that an object, given enough speed, will "fall" around Earth, pulled by gravity out of the straight-line path it would otherwise follow. Today, we are highly dependent on satellites for communications, weather prediction, navigation, science, and other applications.

II. To review, ideas about motion evolved until, by Newton's time, all motion in the universe was assumed to be governed by the same deterministic laws.

III. The Principle of Galilean (Newtonian) Relativity (we might call it the "original principle of relativity").

 A. The laws of motion are the same for anyone, provided that he or she is in uniform motion.

 B. Such statements as "I am moving" or "I am at rest" have no absolute meaning; they are only meaningful when they are about motion or rest *relative* to something else.

C. There are many ways to say this! Remember the cruise ship, Venus, and the distant galaxy. There is simply no experiment you can do in, say, a uniformly moving cruise ship, train, plane, or even planet that will answer for you the question "am I moving?" (You can answer the question "Am I moving relative to Earth, or to my star, or to whatever?"— but that's a question about *relative* motion, not *absolute* motion.)

Essential Reading:

Mook and Vargish, *Inside Relativity*, Chapter 1, Sections 6–8; Chapter 2, Sections 1–5.

Hoffmann, *Relativity and Its Roots*, Chapter 3.

Suggested Reading:

Einstein and Infeld, *The Evolution of Physics*, Chapter 1, pp. 34–67.

Questions to Consider:

1. Many people think astronauts in an orbiting spacecraft are "weightless" because "there's no gravity in space." How is this view inconsistent with Newton's ideas of gravity and motion?

2. You're on a plane flying through calm air. You eat, read, and relax just as you would on the ground—you can't tell that you're "moving." Yet when you look out the window, you see the ground slipping backwards. Why can't you conclude definitely that you and the plane are "moving"? What can you conclude?

Orbits

Newton's thought experiment describes the motion of an object when thrown off a very tall mountain.
Object 1, thrown with modest force falls in a curved path toward the earth.
Object 2, thrown with greater force, falls farther than object one, but still eventually falls to earth.
Object 3, thrown with such force that it falls towards the earth at the same rate that the earth is
curving away beneath it, describes a circular orbit. Absent air resistance or other mitigating
factors, it will continue in this circular motion forever.

39

Lecture Three—Transcript
The Clockwork Universe

Welcome to Lecture Three: "The Clockwork Universe." Why that title? Because part way through this lecture, I hope to convince you that if you believe the Newtonian paradigm of physics, the essence of classical physics, you'll believe that the universe is completely deterministic, that whatever conditions were established at the start, the universe then would evolve like a giant clockwork with every move of every particle completely and inexorably determined. The clockwork universe.

Before we get into the mechanism of the clockwork universe, let's look a little bit about the individual whose name is most associated with this idea, and that's Sir Isaac Newton. I advertised that I would get in the personal touch, occasionally. And I'll do that a little bit in Newton's case.

Newton was born in 1642, which, coincidentally, is the year Galileo died. But he very much carried on where Galileo left off and extended Galileo's ideas. And the physics of Newton is really the physics of Newton and Galileo in many ways. Newton had some interesting history. In his early twenties he had to leave Cambridge University because of the plague. And he actually moved back to his family place in Woolsthorpe, England. And he spent several years there, which were among the most productive years of his life. So the plague drove him away from Cambridge, and he was very productive.

He returned to Cambridge and the Chair that he held is now held by Professor Stephen Hawking, who many of you know about. You may have read his book, *A Brief History Of Time*. So Hawking holds Newton's Chair at Cambridge University. What Newton is most famous for are his laws of motion and his law of gravity. I want to spend most of this lecture looking at those laws, but then at the end, getting us to a sense of how they're going to lead us on to Einstein's relativity.

Newton's three laws of motion are something everybody studies who deals with introductory physics. There are three laws that describe how objects move in response to forces, that is, to pushes and pulls. And together, if you know the pushes and pulls and you know

Newton's laws of motion, then you can determine exactly what an object is going to do. Hence, the clockwork universe idea.

So, what are Newton's three laws of motion? Well, the first is something we've already seen. The first law of motion is essentially the law of inertia that I described in the last lecture and attributed to Galileo. And it says, basically, in somewhat formal terms that an object moves uniformly. And again, remember what uniform motion means. Uniform motion means it's a straight-line path and it's at constant speed. Any deviation in direction or speed is not uniform motion. An object moves uniformly, that is, in a straight line at constant speed, unless it's acted on by a force. That is, by a push or a pull. And we call this the law of inertia. And it's the statement, basically, that straight-line motion at constant speed, uniform motion, is the natural state of motion.

So, here Newton is simply recapitulating what Galileo said—that objects have inertia, and that inertia keeps them moving, makes uniform motion a natural state of motion. And that you have to do something to change that state of motion. You have to exert a force, a push or a pull, to start an object moving, to stop an object moving, to change its speed, or to change its direction. That's the first law of motion.

The second law is the really meaty one. The second law describes quantitatively how forces, that is, pushes and pulls, cause changes in motion. The first law is really a subset of the second law. Because the first law says unless there is a force there won't be a change in motion. Motion will continue in the absence of a force.

Newton's second law quantifies that with the famous formula $F=ma$. And I'm not big on math here, but I do want to describe for you what that formula means. F is the force, the push or the pull; a is the acceleration, the rate at which the object's motion is changing. That's what acceleration means. When you step on the accelerator of your car, what that does is change your speed.

When you turn the steering wheel—this is less obvious—but the steering wheel is also an accelerator. When you turn the steering wheel, you're changing the direction of your motion, and therefore, you're accelerating your car. You may not be going faster or slower. But you are accelerating because your motion is changing; a is the acceleration—the change in motion.

And *m* is the mass. If you will, the weight of the object. And so what the second law says is simply this: Well, first of all, let me tell you what it says in the context of the first law. It says if, after zero, if there is no force, then *a* will be zero. There will be no change in motion. And we get back to the first law that says, absent a force, an object will continue in straight-line motion. There'll be no change in the motion.

But Newton's second law goes beyond that. It tells us, for example, that if *m* is big, if an object is very massive, it would take a big force to give it an acceleration. If an object is not very massive, it doesn't take as much force to give it the same acceleration. As an example, over here I have two objects of different mass. I've got a tennis ball and a basketball. The basketball is not only bigger; it's also more massive. That's the important thing here. And I'm going to give them each the same push. The same acceleration. Here goes the basketball. I'm going to give it a little push. I'm not going to keep pushing it. I don't need to keep pushing it. I'm going to give it a push to change its state of motion. Right now it's at rest with respect to this table. I'm going to change its state of motion. I'm going to make it move with respect to the table. Here I go. I put it into motion. And it then moved in essentially constant motion until another force acted on it—namely me, grabbing it at the other end. So, that was the basketball. Massive. I gave it a force. I didn't change its motion that much. That is, it didn't get moving that fast.

I'm going to give the same sized tap to the tennis ball. Much less mass. Same *F*. Newton's equation says I'm going to get a bigger *a*. It got up to a much greater speed.

Force, mass, and acceleration are related. The bigger the mass, the bigger the force it takes to change an object's motion. And that's true whether you're changing the object's motion, as I did here by changing its speed, by speeding it up, by getting it moving, or changing its motion by stopping it. It takes a bigger force to stop the basketball than it does to stop a rolling tennis ball. It takes a bigger force to stop a truck than it does to stop a car. The acceleration and the force and the mass are all related. And that's what Newton's second law says.

And if we know how an object is accelerating, if we know how its motion is changing and we know how it was initially moving, we can predict everything it's going to do. So, in principle, if you know the force that's acting on an object, the push or pull that's acting on an object, and you know it exactly, and you know what the object is doing at some point, then, in principle, you can predict what it will be doing at every other point in the future. Provided you continue to know the force. That's the essence of the clockwork universe idea. The clockwork universe says, if we know Newton's laws of motion, which we do, and we know the forces, the pushes and pulls, that are acting on objects, and we knew the positions of all the objects that make up the universe, every planet, every electron, every proton, every atom, and we knew their motion, in principle, even though we don't have any computer powerful enough to do the calculation, in principle that calculation is doable. And in principle, everything that happens from then on is predictable. The universe is completely deterministic.

It's kind of a bleak picture, in a sense, philosophically, because it leaves no room for our free will. Unless you want to postulate that our brains operate outside the laws of physics. But that was the picture that emerged from classical physics. A clockwork universe, a universe that once God or some initial, random event, or whatever it is, puts it into motion, the rest of it is completely determined, and it simply runs on its own like a clockwork obeying Newton's laws of motion. Well, that's two of the laws of motion.

The third law of motion you've also heard of. I'm going to phrase it in slightly different terms than you may have heard. Forces come in pairs is what the third law of motion says. It says if I push on something, for example, I'm going to push on this table now, the table pushes back on me. In fact, it pushes back on me with a force that is equal to the force I used in pushing on it. If I push on this lectern, it pushes back on me. And I can feel that push in my hands. When I hit that basketball to get it rolling, I felt that I was hitting it with my hand. That's because the basketball was pushing back on me. That's also an essential part of the set of laws on motion.

For those of you who have studied any physics, the third law of motion is very closely tied with the idea of conservation of momentum. But we don't need to worry about that. The point is, these three laws provide a coherent whole that describe everything there is to know about motion according to Newton, according to classical physics.

So, we have three laws of motion. But we don't yet understand much about the forces, the pushes and pulls, that might act to cause objects' motions to change. Well, there Newton made another great step forward. Newton studied one of the most important forces known.

There is a famous myth about Newton, and we are going to take a look at a picture that describes that myth. Here's a picture of Newton sitting under an apple tree. And the myth goes, apple falls on Newton, hits him on the head, and he discovers gravity. Well, I think that myth stated that way has to be nonsense. It didn't take Newton to discover gravity. It took some cave person sitting under a cliff outside their cave. And rocks come falling down or something. Or a wild animal jumps over the cliff or something. They realize there's gravity. When our ancestors swung from trees, they knew inherently about gravity. You don't discover gravity by having an apple hit you on the head.

The story of Newton, if it's true, is much more subtle, and much more sophisticated, and much more profound in its implications. So, here is Newton sitting under the apple tree. And if this story were true, the moon is also up in the sky at the same time. And Newton sees the moon. And the realization that's associated with the apple tree myth or story, if it's true, is that Newton recognized that the motion of the apple and the motion of the moon are one in the same motion.

That's the essence of Newton's genius. He said, "The moon, what's it doing? It's moving around the Earth. The apple, what's it doing? It's falling toward Earth. What do both those motions have in common?" What they have in common is that in both cases the objects are being accelerated—deviated from straight line, constant speed motion in a direction toward the Earth. It's as though, in both cases, there's a pull toward the Earth acting on both those objects. In the case of the apple, the pull is causing the apple to move, actually physically, toward the Earth. In the case of the moon, the motion is not actually making the moon come any closer to the Earth. But it is pulling it away from its straight line path it would follow according to the first law of motion if there were no force acting on it. That's the key point to realize. It's that simple.

Also, physics is simpler than most people realize. This is a case in point. You ask, what keeps the moon in orbit? What keeps an artificial satellite? And why don't they fall down? They are falling. They're falling toward Earth in the sense that their motion is deviating from a straight line because the Earth is pulling on them. It just happens to be the case with the moon that that pull and the motion of the moon are such that the pull keeps the moon in a circular path.

I have another example of that here. I've got just a tennis ball attached to a string that I'm going to whirl around over my head here, and I'm going to just ask a couple of questions about this. So, here goes the tennis ball. Is it moving in a straight line at a constant speed? No way. It's not moving in a straight line. It may be moving at constant speed, but it's still accelerating, its motion is still changing. It's not going in a straight line at constant speed. It's not undergoing the "natural state of motion." Why isn't it? Because the string is pulling on it, through me, at the center of the string here, pulling. I'm exerting a force, which is communicated through the string to the ball. And the ball is going on a path that deviates, always, from the straight line it would go if I were to let it go flying off, which I won't do. But if the string were cut or something, or I let go, it would go flying off in a straight line at constant speed. It's falling, if you will, toward my hand. It's being pulled, always, toward my hand out of the straight-line path it would otherwise follow.

It's that simple. Objects move in a straight line at constant speed unless they are acted on by a pull. In this case, the pull has just the right strength to keep the object moving in a circular path. And so it does. It deviates from the straight-line path it would otherwise follow. And the moon, in its orbit around the Earth, is doing exactly the same thing. And that is exactly what Newton recognized if, in fact, it's true that the apple hit him on the head and he discovered gravity.

And he didn't only recognize that qualitatively, he recognized it quantitatively as well. He formulated, on the basis of that observation, the so-called law of universal gravitation. Newton said, "I believe every object in the universe attracts every other object with a force, a pull that depends on how massive the two objects are and also on how far apart they are. The further apart they are, the weaker the force." And it falls off very rapidly. It goes as one divided by the square of the distance, if you've heard the inverse square law. We don't need to get in to that. The point is it falls off with distance.

That means the acceleration that the Earth gives to the moon, the great big, massive moon, very far away, is much less than the acceleration it gives to the apple. Why? Because the apple is closer to the Earth. Well, is that true? Newton went and calculated. He said, "What kind of rate of change of motion would it take to cause the moon, roughly 250,000 miles away, to go around the Earth once every, roughly, 27 days?" Which is roughly the period of the moon's orbital motion. And he found that the force was roughly one thirty-six hundredth of the force that acts on the apple. And he calculated that the moon was about 60 times as far from the center of the Earth as the apple is, and that all works with the mathematics of universal gravitation.

So, Newton came up with the law of universal gravitation and demonstrated that it indeed seemed to be true with regard to the apple and the moon. The apple is close to the Earth and falls with a large acceleration. The moon is much further away and "falls"—again, in the sense that it is falling out of the straight line path it would otherwise take in describing a circle—with an acceleration that is weaker in just the exact relation that Newton's law predicts, given how far away it is.

By the way, universal gravitation really has been verified in the laboratory with very delicate apparatus. We can now do experiments where objects like this tennis ball and this basketball—we typically use lead objects or steel objects or something because they'd be more dense and more massive—over scales like this we can measure the strength of the gravitational attraction. In fact, that was first done in the 1700s by Cavendish. So this is an experiment we could actually do. We can measure the universal gravitation between two ordinary sized objects. It's very, very small and very difficult to measure.

When we accumulate a lot of matter in one place as we do with the planet Earth, star, then gravity becomes a big significant force. It's actually rather weak, but it's one of the fundamental forces that makes the universe work—one of the fundamental pushes and pulls.

Newton realized something else with his universal gravitation. He realized the possibility that we could have objects in orbit. And Newton had a thought experiment. He imagined the Earth with a giant mountain on it. Again, one of these thought experiments where you think about what would happen if you could do something, which maybe it's not so easy to do. So we have a picture here of the Earth with a giant mountain on it. We're going to throw a ball, horizontally, off that mountain, and it's going to fall to Earth. Very familiar with that. If I threw that tennis ball, it would fall to the ground pretty soon. If I threw it horizontally, it would describe a curved path. Well, this ball we throw off this high mountain, also describes a curved path. The only difference is, the Earth is curving away beneath it. So it perhaps goes in a slightly different route and lands somewhere else than it would if the Earth had been completely flat. But it goes around and eventually hits the Earth. If we throw it faster, it goes farther before it hits the ground. Just like if I threw a tennis ball horizontally in this studio, it would go further before it hit the ground. But if I throw it fast enough—and here's what Newton's genius again realized—it could be falling toward the Earth at exactly the same rate that the Earth is, if you will, falling away underneath it, because the Earth is curved, and it would go in a circular path and come right back to its starting point. And, absent air resistance or other factors that would tend to slow it down, that ball that we threw would continue in a circular orbit around the Earth forever. It would never stop. In fact, that was Newton's realization. That we could, perhaps, put artificial satellites in orbit. And, today, of course, we do that all the time. And we rely on those satellites for weather prediction and communication and television and navigation—global positioning system receivers in our car these days. All these are examples of satellite technologies. And it was Newton's genius to realize that such satellites were possible. He didn't have the technology to put them up. And it was not until the middle of the twentieth century that we were able to do that. But we routinely put satellites up. And we not only put them in circular orbits, we also put them in elliptical orbits. And Newton also anticipated that.

Newton took his newly discovered universal law of gravitation and he said to himself, what kind of paths will objects follow. What kind of paths, particularly, will a planet follow as it moves in the vicinity of the sun subject to this force, which gets stronger as it gets closer to the sun and weaker as it gets further away. And Newton said, "How do I figure that out?" Well, he discovered he didn't know how to figure that out so he had to invent the branch of mathematics that it takes to figure that out. And that branch of mathematics is called calculus. So Newton had a real incentive to invent calculus, which was also independently invented by Leibnitz.

But Newton invented calculus because he wanted to understand how his universal gravitation would describe the motions of planets. And lo and behold, out of that mathematics came the prediction that the motions of planets should be elliptical orbits. The sun should be at one focus of the ellipse. And the laws that Kepler had described about how fast the planets move around the sun or how much area they sweep out and, the period in relation to the radius of the orbit, size of the elliptical orbit, all those laws that Kepler had described with no physical basis, fell out of Newton's universal gravitation when he applied the calculus and asked the question, how will a planet move in the vicinity of the sun.

So Newton had brilliantly verified Kepler's observations that the planets moved in elliptical orbits. Newton had explained it. He had said the law of universal gravitation—that all objects attract with this force that depends on distance—explains that. So Newton had made a brilliant explanation.

Well, Newton had done more than that. He made a philosophical leap. Because in recognizing that the motion of the moon and the motion of the apple are the same thing, Newton had forever unified terrestrial and celestial motion. That distinction that I emphasized with the ancients, that distinction is gone. No longer do we have a separate law of physics for the crude, base Earth and a different law for the perfect, ethereal heavens up here. They're all described by the same law. It happens to be Newton's universal law of gravitation, coupled with his three laws of motion. They describe the motion of the apple on Earth. They describe the motion of a ball I throw here in this room. They describe the motion of the moon around the Earth, the Earth around the sun, the sun around the center of the galaxy, and an artificial satellite around the Earth. They described motion in the heavens, and they described motion on Earth. And those realms are no longer distinct.

Before we go on, let's just take a moment and review the evolution to this point because now we're quite advanced, beyond the stage of Aristotle. We now have a universal physics. We have laws that seem to govern the behavior of motion everywhere in the universe. Something very different from what Aristotle posited. And those laws are thought out mathematically. They're written in rigorous mathematical language. So we can make predictions, and those predictions agree with reality, as in the case of Newton comparing the acceleration of the moon and the acceleration of the apple, or Newton predicting the motion of a planet and discovering it was exactly what Kepler had described with no basis for understanding why that description was true. Newton has now explained it. So we have a very powerful statement about how the world works, and it seems to apply everywhere in the universe.

So, let's take a look at the history that got us there. We had a natural state of motion, in the case of Aristotle in around 350 B.C., that was rest on Earth. Terrestrial motion, in a natural state, was being at rest on Earth. In the celestial motion, the natural state of motion was circular. And Earth was at the center. Ptolemy embellished that a little bit with the circles on circles, but it was the same basic idea. Natural state of motion, terrestrial, is at rest. Natural state of motion, circular, is the Earth at the center.

We next went to Copernicus, in around 1540, he didn't change the ideas of motion on Earth, but told us that the natural state of motion in the heavens was still circular, but the sun was at the center. So, a step away from the Earth being special, but a conservatism also in maintaining the notion of circular motion.

Galileo comes along, working around the year 1600 and made a radical change in the natural state of motion on Earth. For Galileo, for the first time, the natural state of motion was uniform motion in a straight line. Galileo stated the law of inertia, which became Newton's first law of motion, which was then embellished in Newton's second law to give it a quantitative substance and talk about how forces, how pushes and pulls, change one's state of motion. Galileo, also, in the celestial realm, set the groundwork for Newton by saying the celestial realm is imperfect. I see a miniature planetary system in Jupiter and its moons. I see blemishes on the sun. I see sunspots. I see Venus's phases. And I see the size of Venus changing with phase. And I interpret that to be evidence that, in fact, the Copernican system with the sun at the center seems to be correct.

Then along comes Newton, working around the year 1700, a little earlier, a little later. He says terrestrial and celestial motion, for the first time, obey the same physical laws. Same laws. One universal physics that applies everywhere in the universe. So Newton has done the first of the several great syntheses we're going to talk about in this course. Taking seemingly disparate regions, disparate areas, and disparate fields—in this case astronomy and terrestrial physics—and uniting them. They're one. They're one because they obey the same laws. They can be understood as aspects of the same thing. What Venus is doing in its motion around the sun can be understood as the same thing as what the apple is doing when it falls on Newton's head, or what the tennis ball is doing when you hit it on your game of tennis on the cruise ship. Major philosophical shift. One universal set of laws of physics. And there is something very special about those laws—the Newtonian laws of motion. The Newtonian/Galilean scheme. And I want to take the last few minutes of this lecture and emphasize that very important special point.

Let's ask the question, for whom do these laws of motion work? For whom are Newton's laws true? Just for Newton? No. They're true for anyone. Are they true just on Earth? No. Look at the creature on Jupiter, if there is one, who sees these moons going around. That creature, if a Jovian fruit falls on their head, if there's such a thing as a Jovian, they're going to make the same conclusion. The same laws work on Jupiter as they work on Earth. The same laws work on Venus. We already know this. We were doing this tennis thing on Venus bouncing a tennis ball back and forth. We understand that the laws of physics that work on Earth work elsewhere. And, equally importantly, they work regardless of your state of motion. That's the important point. Not so much your place, but your state of motion.

And I now want to get a little more specific about that and be a little bit more careful when I make that statement. The statement I want to make is this: The statement is that the laws of motion are the same for everyone. At this point I have to qualify that statement somewhat further. And until the year 1914, we're going to keep that qualification on. That qualification applies to Newtonian physics. And it also applies to Einstein's special relativity. It's an important qualification. And it says this: The laws of physics are the same for everybody in uniform motion. Everybody who is in uniform motion. If you're moving in straight line motion at constant speed and you do experiments to determine what are the laws that govern physics, you'll get the same, govern motion anyway, you'll get the same answers that I do if I'm sitting at rest on Earth, or if I'm in a spaceship in interstellar space—without my engine going so I'm not accelerating, so my motion isn't changing—or I'm on that planet, in that distant galaxy, moving away from Earth at 80 percent of the speed of light. As long as we're moving uniformly, we'll get the same results for the laws of motion. We'll all agree that Newton's laws work, that universal gravitation works, and that they have exactly the same form. We could read the same textbooks, and do the same physics, and we'll get it all right.

You may be wondering to yourself, "Wait a minute. Earth isn't in uniform motion. It's spinning. And it's going around the sun." And you're right. Earth isn't exactly in uniform motion. But the spinning of the Earth is slow enough, and the motion around the sun, well, that's a little more subtle. In the context of Newton's theory, I'm going to say that's also slow enough. That Earth is approximately in uniform motion. It's not in a perfect state of uniform motion. And later in the course, in Lecture Eleven, no, Lecture Thirteen rather, we are going to be very, very concerned about how we find a perfect state of uniform motion. And I'll give you an answer to that at that time. But for now, accept that Earth, and the other planets, and the sun, which is going in a very big, slow orbit every 250 million years around the center of the galaxy, these are essentially in uniform motion. Close enough. Newton's laws hold almost perfectly. Go on a rotating merry-go-round, or in a car rounding a corner at high speed or something, or in a car that's accelerating, or a jet plane when it's heading down the runway, and Newton's laws distinctly don't apply in those environments because those are not situations where you're in uniform motion. But here at the surface of the Earth, we're close enough. Not perfect. But close enough. And so, we have this principle that the laws of motion are the same for anyone in uniform motion. And I spent a good part of the end of the first lecture convincing you that you, in your gut, know that. And it makes a lot of good sense to you. It would be a ridiculous universe in which we had these nice, simple laws of motion that worked only here on Earth. And if you go to Venus, there's something more complicated, and if you go to the distant planet, on that distant galaxy, it's even more complicated. No way. It makes good physical sense. The laws of motion, and I'm going to emphasize motion, I'm going to use the word motion, instead of physics, for the next few lectures, because at the time of Newton, motion was the only branch of physics really known to any great extent. We knew a little bit about optics. A little bit about heat. But not a whole lot. Motion. It's the laws of motion that are the same for anyone in uniform motion. And that statement has a name. It's called the *Principle of Galilean Relativity.*

Sometimes called *Newtonian Relativity*, because it flows out of the ideas of Newton and Galileo.

This is the first time we've seen the word relativity in a real physics context. I've talked about relativity before, how this is going to be a course, largely, about Einstein's relativity. Here's that word "relativity" cropping up. Einstein's relativity is actually not such a new idea. It's actually a very old idea recycled and embellished a little bit. We're going to come to understand that in a few lectures. The original relativity principle was Galileo's and Newton's. It's the Principle of Galilean Relativity, and it states what I just said. It says the laws of motion are the same for anyone provided they're in uniform motion. And that's a kind of formal way of saying it.

There are lots of other ways of saying it, of which I'll just give you a few examples. You can play tennis on a cruise ship, or on Venus, or on this distant planet orbiting a star in a galaxy that's so far away that it's moving away from us at 80 percent of the speed of light. These all make good, gut sense. As long as the motion is uniform. If the cruise ship gets hit by a tidal wave, things get real different. If Venus crashes into another planet and breaks in pieces, or something, or if you're in an airplane and it encounters turbulence, then it doesn't apply because those aren't uniform motion. But you could play tennis on a cruise ship, or on Venus, or on that distant planet. It's all the same. Because the laws of motion work for you just as well there and in that state of motion as they do here on Earth. Other ways to say it: Only relative motion matters. If you say to me, if you're driving down the road at constant speed in a straight line and I'm standing by the roadside, I'm prone to say you're moving. But you have every right to say, no. I'm just sitting here in my car, you're moving the other way. We tend to be very prejudiced to thinking the Earth is this special place. And so whoa, it's really the person who knows Earth that is at rest and the other person moving. But what Galilean relativity, not anything fancy, and Einsteinian, just old-fashioned Galilean and Newtonian motion theory tells us is that you really can't distinguish. We can't say one person is moving and one is not. Anyone in uniform motion has equal access to the laws of physics. They are equally good for anyone in uniform motion, and so no one can say, absolutely, I am moving and you are at rest, or I'm at rest and you're moving. Those statements make no sense.

What we can say is I'm moving down the highway at 50 miles per hour relative to the ground. Or, you're moving—you standing at rest relative to the Earth—are moving past me at 50 miles an hour the other way. We can talk about relative motion. That's why it's a relativity principle. Because it says relative motion is a meaningful concept, but absolute motion is not. Only relative motion matters. That's what that statement means. You can eat dinner on an airplane because you don't worry about the fact your food is moving at 600 miles an hour. As long as the plane is moving uniformly, no problem. You put your fork in the food, just like you would at home, and you eat the food. Now, you hit turbulence and the food goes flying all over the place. That's different. You're no longer in uniform motion and the laws don't apply there. I am moving is a meaningless statement. You can say, I'm moving relative to you, but you can't say, I am moving. That's a meaningless statement. And to put it more succinctly in the final terms, and we're going to come back to the statement again and again in the next few lectures, there is simply no experiment you can do involving the laws of motion that will answer the question, am I moving? Put you in that airplane. Pull down all the shades so you can't see the Earth going by, and there is no way you can tell, for sure, whether or not the airplane is moving or not.

There's no experiment you can do with tennis balls and billiard balls, and throwing things around and measuring forces and pushes and pulls that will give you any sense of physics other than Newton's laws of motion. There's no experiment you can do that will answer the question, am I moving? And that's where we sit at Newton's classical physics with a law of relativity, a principle of relativity that says, uniform motion is the natural state, and motion doesn't matter. As long as you're in uniform motion, we all see the same laws of physics.

Lecture Four
Let There Be Light!

Scope:

The study of motion is not all there is to physics. The ancient Greeks and Chinese knew, respectively, about electricity and magnetism. By the eighteenth century, scientists engaged in serious experimental studies of electricity and magnetism. The two phenomena turned out to be related; magnetism can produce electrical effects and vice versa. Today, electromagnetism is known to be responsible for the chemical interactions of atoms and molecules, all of modern electronic technology, and most other phenomena of everyday experience
and of technology.

The effects of electricity and magnetism are best described by positing electric and magnetic *fields* that exert forces on matter. It is an observed fact that a changing magnetic field can produce an electric field; this interaction is at the basis of electric power generation and information retrieval from videotapes and computer disks. In the 1860s, James Clerk Maxwell suggested that a changing electric field should, similarly, produce a magnetic field. Maxwell showed that a consequence of his suggestion is the existence of *electromagnetic waves*—structures of linked electric and magnetic fields that travel through empty space. Maxwell calculated the speed of such waves in terms of quantities that appear in electromagnetic theory, and the result turned out to be *the known speed of light*! Maxwell concluded that light is an electromagnetic wave and, thus, that optical phenomena ultimately involve electromagnetism.

Outline

I. A new branch of physics: electricity and magnetism.

   A. Early experiments with static electricity showed that electric charge is a fundamental property of matter. Like charges repel; opposites attract.

   B. Early experiments with magnets showed that all magnets have two poles. Like poles repel; opposite poles attract.

   C. The *field concept* describes electric and magnetic interactions in terms of invisible *fields* that exert forces on

charges
and magnets.

1. This view contrasts with the earlier *action-at-a-distance* concept, in which electric charges and magnets somehow "reach out" across empty space to influence other charges or magnets.
2. Experiments led to two laws showing how electric and magnetic fields arise from electric charges and magnets, respectively.
3. The field concept can also be applied to gravitational attraction.

II. Electricity and magnetism are intimately related; hence, *electromagnetism.*

A. A moving electric charge produces magnetism—a phenomenon at the basis of many technologies, including electric motors. The electrons moving in atoms constitute moving electric charge that is the ultimate source of magnetism in magnetic materials.

B. Changing magnetic fields produce electric fields—a phenomenon at the basis of computer disks, audio and videotapes, and electric power generators.

C. In the 1860s, Maxwell suggested that if magnetic fields produce electric fields, why not the opposite as well? Maxwell incorporated this suggestion into the laws of electromagnetism, completing four equations that describe all electromagnetic phenomena.

D. Maxwell showed that his equations implied the existence of *electromagnetic waves*, structures of electric and magnetic fields that travel through empty space.

1. He calculated the speed of such waves from quantities appearing in his equations and found it was equal to the known speed of light!
2. He concluded that light must be an electromagnetic wave, making optical science a branch of electromagnetism.
3. Other electromagnetic waves now known include radio, infrared, ultraviolet, x-rays, and gamma rays, which differ in their frequencies (and therefore wavelengths).

E. In 1887, Heinrich Hertz generated and received electromagnetic waves in a laboratory, and in 1901, Guglielmo Marconi transmitted radio waves across the Atlantic Ocean.

Essential Reading:

Mook and Vargish, *Inside Relativity*, Chapter 2, Section 7.

Hey and Walters, *Einstein's Mirror*, Chapter 2, through p. 29.

Suggested Reading:

Einstein and Infeld, *The Evolution of Physics*, Chapter 2, through p. 33.

Casper and Noer, *Revolutions in Physics*, Chapter 12.

Questions to Consider:

1. Why was Maxwell's assertion that a changing electric field should produce a magnetic field crucial to the existence of electromagnetic waves?

2. Maxwell's realization that the phenomena of optics can be explained by electromagnetism is an example of scientific synthesis, in which hitherto unrelated phenomena are found to be related. What are some other examples of such syntheses?

Maxwell's Equations

And God said...

Equation	What it says...
$\nabla \cdot \mathbf{E} = \dfrac{\rho}{\varepsilon_0}$	How charges attract/repel
$\nabla \cdot \mathbf{B} = 0$	No isolated magnetic poles
$\nabla \times \mathbf{E} = -\dfrac{\partial \mathbf{B}}{\partial t}$	Changing magnetism produces electricity
$\nabla \times \mathbf{B} = \mu_0 \mathbf{J} + \mu_0 \varepsilon_0 \dfrac{\partial \mathbf{E}}{\partial t}$	Changing electricity produces magnetism

...and there was light.

Lecture Four—Transcript
Let There Be Light!

Welcome to lecture number four: "Let There Be Light!" This lecture will be an attempt to give you, in half an hour, what I normally teach in an entire semester, namely, the subject of electricity and magnetism.

If motion were all there were to the study of physics, our story of the history of physics before relativity would be essentially over. But there's a whole other branch of physics—electricity and magnetism—that actually was known about for a long, long time. The ancient Greeks coined the word electron for the substance amber, which, because it's a very good insulator of electricity, somewhat like Styrofoam, tends to exhibit a lot of static electricity and things cling to it the way socks cling to each other today when they come out of the dryer, for example.

The ancient Chinese also knew about magnetism. And magnetic compasses were already in use by the twelfth century. Nevertheless, in terms of a rigorous base of knowledge on electromagnetism, electricity and magnetism came after mechanics, after the study of motion. And we need to take a look at electricity and magnetism because relativity, really, more than most people realize, is a direct outgrowth of the study of electricity and magnetism, and the questions that were asked about it in relation to the kinds of questions we've already asked about the study of motion. So, we want to spend most of this lecture looking briefly at the subject of electricity and magnetism, and, in the end, coming to a very important conclusion from that subject, and a conclusion that you'll need to realize is true. You'll need to appreciate it. And you'll need to grasp its significance if we're going to go forward and understand where relativity comes from.

So, I want to begin with just a brief description of some early experiments with electricity. People studied things like they would rub a piece of glass with the fur of a cat. And something would stick to it, little particles of dust or paper would stick to it. You've seen things like this happen. You rub a balloon and you can stick it on the wall. This was the phenomenon of static electricity.

And through a number of experiments like this people gradually realized that a property called electric charge is a fundamental aspect of matter. And that electric charge comes in two varieties. And it was Ben Franklin, the American statesperson, who actually studied this in some detail and coined the terms positive and negative for those two kinds of electric charge. There's nothing positive about positive charge, and nothing missing about negative charge. They're just two words for two basic, fundamental properties of matter.

If you ask me as a physicist what charge is, I'm going to have to say I really don't know. It's a fundamental property of matter. The most basic particles we know about—the electrons and the quarks, more about them later in the course—they have electric charge. Some have positive charge. Some have negative charge. We don't know what charge is. It's a fundamental property.

If you ask me what mass is or weight, I don't really understand what that is either. But I know what it is from feeling heavier objects and lighter objects. And, similarly, from doing experiments with electricity and magnetism, and from building electromagnetic devices, we have a feel for what electric charge is. It's a fundamental property of matter. And one important aspect of electric charge is that like charges—imagine these two tennis balls are two identical electric charges—like charges repel. So it's hard to push like charges together. They want to fly apart. There's a repulsive force between them. It's actually somewhat similar to the gravitational force that Newton came up with centuries ago. It falls off in strength with the inverse square of the distance between the objects. So, when they're far apart they don't feel much force. When they're close together they feel a very big, strong force. The force is repulsive if the two charges are the same. The force is attractive if the two charges are different. A positive and a negative charge will be attracted together. And, absent any other forces, they will simply come together. So, like charges repel. Opposite charges attract.

That's not something we can have with gravity, because there's only one kind of matter. One kind of mass. It's all positive, basically, and masses all attract each other.

But electricity works a little bit differently. There are two kinds of charge. Opposite charges attract. Like charges repel. So, that was basic knowledge of electricity.

And in the 1700s and into the 1800s, people experimented with other aspects of electricity. They developed batteries. They could make electric current flow through wires. Frogs legs twitched when touched with pieces of metal. And that led to the discovery of the battery and to electric currents and everything we know today about electric circuits. So, there is a lot of work being done in the 1700s, early 1800s, on the study of electricity.

Now, I'm using the word electricity here. The title of my lecture, "Let There Be Light!" I then introduced as a lecture about electromagnetism, or electricity and magnetism. But, so far, I've said only electricity.

People also knew about magnets and magnetism. And I have here a couple of magnets, and I just want to review what you probably already know about magnets. The typical magnet has two ends called poles—north and south. And magnets have the properties that north and south poles are attracted. So, if I bring the north pole of this magnet and the south pole of this magnet together, they come together. And it takes work to pull them apart. And then that force falls off rapidly as I move them further and further apart. Here, I feel no force between them. Here, I just begin to feel an attractive force. Here, they come together, and they come very closely together, and are attracted.

If I turn one of the magnets around, so I'm putting two south poles together, now I get a repulsive interaction. Again, opposites attracting, likes repelling. So here we go—two likes. I try to push them together, and it gets very hard to do. They want to fly apart. So we have these magnets with their poles—like poles repel, opposite poles attract—similar to what happens with electric charge.

But magnetism is not electricity. Magnets are not electric charges. The ends of the magnets are not charged. We seem to have two different phenomena. We have the phenomenon of electricity that involves this fundamental property of matter—electric charge—and we have the phenomenon of magnetism that seems to involve things like magnets. And, by the way, there are naturally occurring materials that are magnetic.

Before I go on and introduce the idea of electromagnetism, let me say a little bit more about how we conceptualize this interaction between either electric charges or electricity or magnetic pulls. Here are two electric charges. One of them is positive and one of them is negative, say. As I described their interaction, I said, okay these two charges are attracted to each other. The green one exerts a force on the yellow one. The yellow one exerts a force on the green one. Newton's third law, by the way, tells us that whatever force the green one exerts on the yellow one, the yellow one exerts an equal and opposite force on the green one. That was Newton's third law. And they come together.

There's a problem with that, a philosophical problem, and also a mathematical problem, with trying to describe the interaction that way. When I say the green charge exerts a force on the yellow charge, I'm saying that somehow this green charge reaches out across empty space and grabs onto this yellow one. Now, how does that happen? Newton called that "action at a distance." How does "action at a distance" happen? How does an object that's way over here exert an influence on one that's over here? And a particularly disturbing question about that issue is this: What if this one suddenly disappeared? Suddenly disappeared. Ceased to exist. Would the yellow one know that immediately? Would it know immediately to stop feeling an attractive force in this direction? Or wouldn't it?

And if you want to go to a bigger picture, imagine we are talking about gravity. And this is the Earth. And this is the moon. And if the Earth suddenly disappeared, would the moon know immediately to stop moving around in its orbit? How did that information get to it? It's a problem. It's going to be a big problem when we get to relativity and we find we don't want there to be ways where information can get from one place to another instantaneously. So this description of the electric interaction or the magnetic interaction in terms of a force that somehow reaches out across a distance and pulls on the other object—there is something a little bothersome about it, philosophically.

There's also a bit of a problem mathematically, which really isn't as deep a problem, but still bothered people. And that is this: Here's this green charge—positive or negative, I haven't decided which, but it's one of those two. And it's attracting this yellow charge, which is the opposite. What if I took the yellow charge away and put another green charge there? Well, then it would be repelled. And I'd have to describe the interaction all over again. What I'd really like to know is, what electrical influence does this charge exert on objects I might put anywhere in its vicinity? And there's a way to describe that with a new concept. And it's a somewhat abstract concept, but it's important to understand it for purposes of this lecture and then what follows. And the idea is the field, the *field of force*. And I'm going to introduce the field of force, first in terms of gravity and then go back and describe it in terms of electricity and magnetism.

Let me use gravity as an example. This is now not going to be a charge but what it is—a tennis ball. Again, there are two ways of describing the interaction between this tennis ball and the Earth. One is to say the Earth, way down there, all the mass that makes up the Earth—the stuff right below the floor, Mount Everest, on the other side of the planet, all the water in the Pacific Ocean, all the water in the Atlantic Ocean, the continent of North America, the continent of Africa, all the ice in Antarctica—all those aspects of the Earth reach out and pull on this tennis ball, and somehow result in a force, which beautifully—and Newton proved this to be the case—is directed toward the center of the Earth. And as a result, the tennis ball falls. The Earth reaches out, pulls on it, and down it goes. Not just the Earth right here, but all parts of the Earth. And similarly, by Newton's third law and by the universal law of gravitation, the tennis ball reaches out on all parts of the Earth and pulls on them. And the net result is a force upward on the Earth.

It's just the Earth is so massive. Force equals mass times acceleration. Its motion hardly changes. When I let go of the tennis ball—because of the force of the tennis ball and the Earth, the tennis ball is very light—its motion changes fairly dramatically when I let it go, and it falls to Earth.

But they're actually both pulling on each other. And the action at a distance view would say the Earth reaches out and grabs on the tennis ball. Earth reaches out and grabs on the moon. Earth reaches out and grabs on a satellite and exerts a force that swings in its orbit.

The field concept says, "No, there's a more sophisticated way of looking at that." And the more sophisticated way is to say the Earth creates in its vicinity a thing called a field of force. In this case, a gravitational field. At every point in the Earth's vicinity there exists this invisible entity. The gravitational field. And it has the property that if I put matter there, that matter will experience a force. The stronger the gravitational field, the stronger the force it will experience. And the bigger the mass of the object, also the bigger the force it will experience. And the direction of the gravitational field— it has a direction—is directed toward the center of the Earth. So there's a gravitational field right at this point, and it's directed toward the center of the Earth. And there's a gravitational field right at this point, and it's directed toward the center of the Earth. And there's a gravitational field above Antarctica, which is directed in a different way—toward the center of the Earth, but that's a different direction, at Antarctica. And you could imagine the entire Earth surrounded by these invisible arrows, almost, that describe the strength of the gravitational field and tell us what would happen if we put an object there.

What do we gain by this picture? Well, one thing we gain is a description of the Earth's gravity independent of particular objects like tennis balls, or the moon, or satellites that I might choose to put there. The other thing we gain is a way around that philosophical problem I described earlier. Because if the Earth suddenly disappeared, this description says that doesn't mean the gravitational field that the Earth created in space around it disappears immediately. It takes time for that information about the Earth disappearing to get out to the moon. It takes time for the moon suddenly to stop moving in its circular orbit and go in the straight line it goes in if there's no force acting on it.

So, the field concept describes an interaction between two objects—a gravitational interaction in this case, an interaction involving gravity—in a very different way. It says a gravitating object, like the Earth, creates a gravitational field all through space, surrounding it. And objects respond to the gravitational field, not somewhere far away, but in their immediate vicinity. This tennis ball doesn't need to know about the Earth and Mount Everest. It needs to know about the gravitational field they've created at this point in space. The field idea is a local idea. It says objects behave the way they do because of their local environment. Now, that local environment is shaped by the distant parts of the Earth. But it's nevertheless the local environment to which the tennis ball responds.

It's the same thing with electricity and magnetism. Let's go back again to these being two charges. The old fashioned action at a distance description would say the green one reaches out, exerts a force on the yellow one, and pulls it. The yellow one reaches out, exerts a force on the green one, pulls it. They come together. The field concept says nope. The green one creates a field at all points in space. In this case, an electric field, because this is electrically charged. It's a force field. And if I put some other charged object in its vicinity, it will experience a force that depends on the electric field right where I put it. Now that electric field arose, came about, because of the presence of the green one. But, again, there's that philosophical distinction. The force on the yellow one arises because of what's happening in its immediate vicinity. Namely, there's an electric field of force there. I put any charge there, it will experience a force that depends on how charged it is and on how strong that field is.

Similarly, if I want to talk about magnetism, I can say that this magnet creates a field of force. And if you've ever seen the demonstration where a magnet is plunked down on a pile of iron filings, they line up to create a visual picture of that field of force. Which way it points. There's a field of force surrounding this magnet. If I put another magnet somewhere in that vicinity, that other magnet experiences that field of force and gets a force exerted on it. And that's a description of the magnetic interaction.

So, it's very abstract sounding. But we've gone from the point where we said two objects interact—magnetically, gravitationally, or electrically—because each one pulls or pushes on the other, to saying each object creates this mysterious field in space around it, and the other object responds to that field. Very abstract sounding. But it has a tremendous reality. Because as soon as you acknowledge the existence of these fields, and you study electricity and magnetism a little more, you find these fields, for instance, have energy. They have substance to them, in a sense. We can't see them. We can't touch them. But they're there. And they actually are repositories of energy.

And we find other things about them. We find, in particular, that if we think about the fields, we come to understand a relationship between electricity and magnetism. A really deep and profound relationship. And I want to take a few minutes to describe briefly what some aspects of that relationship are.

It turns out that if I move an electric charge—again, here is my electric charge—if I simply move it along, that creates magnetism. In fact, what's going on inside this magnet is not that there are lots of funny little fundamental magnetic things. But, rather, that there are moving electric charges. There are the electric charges in the atoms that make up this material. And this happens to be a rod of iron, which I've painted one end silver to mark the South Pole and mark things on it. The atoms in iron, in particular, have a property that they all line themselves up so all their little electron motions are going around, basically, together. And that creates a big composite effect of electric charge—moving, which in turn, creates magnetism. So that's where a magnet comes from. It's really arising from moving electric charges.

Similarly, in an electric motor, which is a device you use every day—it runs your refrigerator, it runs your CD player, it runs the fans that keep you cool, it runs your air conditioners, it runs the subway trains you travel in, it runs electric trains, it runs the starter motor of your car, it runs your watch. I could go on, and on, and on, and on. Electric motors simply consist of coils of wire with electric currents flowing through them. They become magnets, and the magnetic forces that are so generated cause them to spin. There's another example where electricity and magnetism are related.

More fundamentally, there's a relationship directly between the electric fields and the magnetic fields. And the relation is something like this: If I have magnetism, if I have a magnetic field arising from, say, a magnet. For example, I'm going to grab this magnet again. This magnet creates a magnetic field in the space around it. If I change that magnetic field in any way, for example by moving the magnet around or something, the fact is that that creates electricity. It creates an electric field. The fields that I've talked about, these abstract entities, have existence of their own, basically.

Changing a magnetic field by moving a magnet creates an electric field. I've got a little demonstration of that here with a device I borrowed from my daughter. It's a flashlight. But it's a very special flashlight because it has no batteries. And I'm going to run this flashlight by cranking the little crank at the bottom. As long as I do that, the flashlight is lit. Now, what I have here is a miniature electric generator. The electricity that runs your televisions, your computers, your refrigerators, all your household lighting, most of our industrial machinery, is generated by large-scale versions of this. And it consists of nothing more than a coil of wire in the presence of a magnet. The coil of wire spins. It senses changing magnetic field, because it's moving in the vicinity of this magnet. And, consequently, changing magnetism creates an electric field. And there are electrons in that wire and they respond to the electric field.

They feel an electric force. And they're driven through the wire and make the electric current that ultimately lights that light bulb. This little device could be an entire course in electromagnetism all itself.

But the point I want to leave you with from this is there is an intimate connection between electricity and magnetism. And the connection is that changing magnetism makes electricity. To be a little more precise about that, a changing magnetic field makes an electric field.

There are many ways to change the magnetic field. I can move a coil of wire around near a magnet. I can wave a magnet in the air like I was doing before. I can turn an electromagnet on or off and that makes a changing magnetic field. In all those cases, I produce electricity.

There are a lot of practical consequences of that. I already described electric generators. But you're all either watching, or listening to this course with video or audio tape. And what's going on there is the information of this course has been impressed as a pattern of magnetization on a thin strip of tape containing metallic oxides that are themselves magnetic. And what's happening in your tape player, whether it's video or audio, is that tape is being moved rapidly past a little coil of wire. And the changing patterns associated with the changing magnetic information on that tape is producing changing electric fields. And those changing electric fields are producing forces on electrons in the coil of wire, and those electrons are flowing in patterns that correspond to the visual appearance of what I'm doing and to the sound of my voice. And that's ultimately being amplified and displayed on your television screen and/or coming out your loud speakers. So audio and video tapes, computer disks, work the same way, your credit card stripe when you swipe your credit card and that magnetic stripe gives out its information, works the same way. The pattern of magnetization on that credit card is swiped past a little coil of wire and the changing magnetization makes electricity.

So a key thing you need to know, without knowing a whole lot more about electricity and magnetism, is that changing magnetism makes electricity. So where are we at this point? Well, we've really seen, sort of, three things. We've seen a brief discussion, not quantitative, no equations or anything, that describes how like charges repel and opposite charges attract. The force between electric charges. We've talked about electricity and described electricity briefly. We've talked about magnetism. We've described how there's an attractive force on opposites and a repulsive force on like poles. We've described magnetism, independent of electricity. So there are two things: I've described electricity, and I've described magnetism. And then I've talked about a relationship between the two, whereby changing magnetism produces electricity, and my little generator-powered flashlight is an example of that.

Something's missing there. Something's missing. I talked about electricity. I talked about magnetism. I talked about a relationship between the two whereby magnetism makes electricity. To be precise, changing magnetism, a changing magnetic field, makes an electric field. Something's missing.

In the 1860s, the Scottish physicist James Clerk Maxwell thought about this a lot. He thought there is something missing here. Now, remember I talked about in the first lecture about how science is a creative activity. It isn't just a bland, go in the laboratory and test your hypothesis kind of activity. Well, Maxwell was displaying the creative, almost aesthetic, side. He said there's something missing. There's not a symmetry there that I kind of expect to see in nature. We know about electricity. We got laws that cover that. We know about magnetism. We got laws that cover that. We know that changing magnetism produces electricity. Why doesn't changing electricity produce magnetism? And Maxwell says, "I think it should."

You know, if I was creating the universe, I would make it that way. It would have more symmetry. It would be more beautiful. There's nothing practical about this. There's nothing technological. This is aesthetics pure and simple. Maxwell said, "I think this should be the case." Now, he had some technical reasons, also, for proposing that. But there was no experimental evidence directly for it.

Maxwell proposed, "I think a changing electric field should also produce a magnetic field." And he formulated then out of what had been known before and this new idea, four laws of electricity and magnetism. And in his honor they are called Maxwell's equations. They represent the second of the great syntheses I've been mentioning in this course. In that synthesis, electricity and magnetism become joined in one subject—electromagnetism. And

I'm going to show you these equations. Not because I want to do lots of mathematics. But because to a physicist they're so beautiful.

So here's a picture showing you Maxwell's equations. On the left, I've got the equations. There are four of them. Don't worry about the funny looking symbols. That's not what I'm trying to impress you with. Although I am trying to impress you with the fact that those four equations tell us everything we physicists need to know about electricity and magnetism. At least, at the level before quantum physics becomes important. In the whole macroscopic realm, from things the size of atoms and on up practically, this describes, basically, everything there is to say about electricity and magnetism.

And there are four of these equations. The first one talks about electricity alone. You see the "E" in the equation, that's for the electricity. You see the "B," sorry about the terminology, but that's for magnetism. So what do these equations say? The first one talks about how charges attract and repel. The second one talks about magnetic poles. They always come in north/south pairs. We won't get into that. It's an interesting fact, has some profound implications. But that's what that one says. It's the last two that are important to us.

The third one says that a changing magnetic field produces an electric field. That funny symbol on the right, with the "B," magnetic field, and the "t," time, talks about changing magnetic fields. And it says that makes electric field. You see that on the left.

The bottom one says what we knew for a long time. Namely, that electric charges in motion create magnetism. That's what the "J" stands for. But it also tells us that changing electric field makes magnetic field. There's the "E" and the "t" on the right. Electricity changing with time. There's the "B," magnetism, on the left.

What's the point of all of this? If you don't know anything else from either this lecture or from a course you might take in electricity and magnetism, come away understanding that changing magnetism makes electricity. And changing electricity makes magnetism. Because Maxwell then went ahead and said, "What are the consequences of this fact?" And he came up with a brilliant prediction. He said, "Look, suppose I had some changing magnetic field. I might make it by taking a magnet and wiggling it a little bit or something. Well, now I have changing magnetic fields here. What do they produce? They produce electric fields. And the likelihood is, depending on how I wiggle this stuff, unless I wiggle it in a very smooth, regular, continuous, steady, fashion, those electric fields will also be changing. And, therefore, what do they produce? They produce changing magnetic field. And what do those changing magnetic fields produce? They produce changing electric fields." And so on.

And Maxwell envisioned, then, there could be a structure of—started out with either electric or magnetic fields, I don't care which— changing, creates changing the other field back and forth. Changing electric, changing magnetic, changing electric, changing magnetic, changing electric. And the thing leap frogs itself through space. It's acquired an independent existence. And it carries with it electromagnetic energy. And it propagates through space as a wave.

Maxwell predicted the existence of electromagnetic waves. And he did something else. He predicted the speed that those waves should travel at. If you look at my picture of Maxwell's equations again, you'll see some funny little Greek letters. There's a mu (μ) and an epsilon (ε). Those are numbers that describe how electricity, the strength of the electric and magnetic fields, behave. Basically, how strong electricity is. How strong magnetism is. They were numbers that were arrived at by laboratory experiments. Doing things like taking a couple of charged objects and measuring how strong the force is. Or taking a current flowing through a wire, an electric current flowing through a wire, and seeing how strong a magnetic field it produces. And so on.

Nothing to do with optics, among other things. Maxwell calculated that the speed of his electromagnetic waves depended on those numbers and nothing else. And he calculated that speed. And it came out to be the known speed of light. Now until this point, nobody knew what light was. People had speculated since about the early 1800s that it was a wave. Newton thought it was a particle. Much more on that later in the course.

But it was known by Maxwell's time that light was a wave. Nobody knew what it was a wave of. All of a sudden, Maxwell, putting together this theory of electricity and magnetism, predicts that there should be waves of electromagnetism. And they should propagate through empty space. They should travel through empty space carrying energy with them—electromagnetic energy with them—and they should do so at the known speed of light. And it immediately became obvious that light was a form of electromagnetic wave.

And Maxwell asked other questions about electromagnetic waves. Are there other forms other than light? And, yes, there are other forms. There are forms like radio waves, and infrared waves, and ultra-violet waves, and x-rays, and gamma rays. These are all electromagnetic waves. They are all basically identical. All that differs in them is how rapidly they vibrate. Light waves vibrate about 10^{14} or 10^{15} times a second. That's a one with 14 or 15 zeros after it, times a second. Radio waves vibrate maybe a million or a hundred million times a second. FM radio is about a hundred million times a second. That's why you tune your dial to a hundred megahertz or 101.5 or whatever. AM radio, tune your dial to 850. That's 850,000 vibrations a second. All those waves are the same. They're basically electromagnetic waves. And they consist of changing electric and magnetic fields. And the important point for our course here is that Maxwell's equations predict the existence of those waves. And equally importantly, predict the speed that those waves should go at.

Today, we know a whole spectrum, as I say, of electromagnetic waves. A whole spectrum from radio waves—the slowest vibrating ones—but they all go at the same speed. It's just a question of how fast the vibrations of the electric and magnetic fields are occurring. The waves themselves are all moving at exactly the same speed. It's the known speed of light. About 186,000 miles a second, 300,000 kilometers a second, or to put it in terms that are better for people who design electric circuits and so on, it's about one foot per nanosecond. So in a nanosecond—a billionth of a second—light goes about one foot. That, by the way, sets a limit to the speed of our computers. Because computers need to move information at speeds that are close to, but can't be faster than, the speed of light for reasons you'll soon see. And, therefore, they can't be very big. If they were too big, they'd be too slow in terms of the time it takes them to get information.

So Maxwell has proven the existence of electromagnetic waves. People set out to prove his hypothesis. And Heinrich Hertz, in 1887, succeeded in generating electromagnetic waves on one side of a laboratory and, with another apparatus on the other side, receiving those waves. So he demonstrated that Maxwell was correct by making, if you will, artificial electromagnetic waves as opposed to the natural ones that are all around us.

That was in 1887. By 1901, the Italian, Marconi, transmitted electromagnetic waves across the Atlantic Ocean for the first time. And so, the electromagnetic wave discovery became a very, very practical thing. And today, electromagnetic waves are used in our cell phones. The mouse I've been clicking to operate my computer visuals over here is transmitting its clicks by electromagnetic waves, by radio waves in that case. All of radio, television, microwaves, infrared devices, all these things, lasers, all these things are generating and using electromagnetic waves.

Electromagnetic waves are ubiquitous. And the important point for us is they all arise in exactly the same way. You somehow make an electric or magnetic field change—maybe by electrons going back and forth in a wire antenna, maybe by doing something to the electrons in atoms, as in a laser—whatever you do, once you've started that process, the electromagnetic wave propagates away, and at least if it's in vacuum, it does so at one unique speed. No matter what kind of wave it is, radio, television, infrared, visible, whatever, x-rays, gamma rays, it goes at the speed which we designate by the letter "c"—186,000 miles a second, a foot per nanosecond, 300,000 kilometers a second.

In fact, if you're religious, and I'm not trying to be religious here, but if you were religious, I think you would embellish Maxwell's equations in the following way. And this way involves the title of my lecture here. Maxwell's equations, if you were creating the universe, and you wanted a universe in which there was going to be light, from what we know of light, you would need to create a universe with electricity and magnetism. A universe that obeyed Maxwell's equations. So if you want to think of it in sort of terms of Genesis, and God said this—all those equations—and there was light. Because that's where light came from. Light comes from electromagnetic waves. Light is electromagnetic waves. It's a result of electromagnetism.

Where are we going with this? What I want you to take away from this lecture is the idea that electromagnetic waves are a necessary consequence of the branch of physics called electromagnetism, and that electromagnetic waves, as predicted by that branch of physics, travel with a known speed. It's the speed of light. It's a known definite number. There's no exceptions to that. Electromagnetic waves, in vacuum, travel with this known speed, which from now on we'll simply call c.

Lecture Five

Speed *c* Relative to What?

Scope:

We now have two branches of physics: the study of motion (also called *mechanics*) and electromagnetism. For mechanics, the Principle of Galilean Relativity holds—meaning that the laws of mechanics are the same for anyone in uniform motion. Is the same true for the laws of electromagnetism? Or, is there some special state of motion (also called a *frame of reference*) that is the only one for which the laws of electromagnetism (Maxwell's equations) are valid? Because Maxwell's equations predict the existence of electromagnetic waves (light) going at speed *c*, the equivalent question is "with respect to what, does light go at speed *c*?"

For other waves, the answer to the question "speed relative to what?" is obvious: for water waves, it's the water; for sound waves, it's the air; for earthquake waves it's the Earth. Each of these waves has a *medium*—water, air, Earth—the disturbance of which constitutes the wave. Nineteenth-century physicists felt the same way about light. They posited a substance called the *ether*, assumed to fill all space, that was the medium for light (and other electromagnetic waves).

Now we have a dichotomy: In mechanics, the relativity principle holds, and all uniformly moving reference frames are equally valid places to study physics. But electromagnetism seems to work only in a frame of reference at rest relative to the ether. Is Earth moving with respect to the ether? Both philosophical considerations and scientific evidence suggest that it must be.

Outline

I. A brief history of physics to the year 1900.

    A. Between approximately 1600 to 1750, Galileo, Newton, and others developed a mechanical understanding of physical reality. The mechanical universe is *deterministic*, and a *relativity principle* holds.

    B. Between approximately 1750 to 1900, Maxwell and others developed an understanding of electromagnetic phenomena, including light.

II. Frames of reference and the validity of physical laws.

    A. A frame of reference is the place that shares your motion (if you're in a car, it's the car; if you're in a plane, it's the plane).

    B. A simple question: In what frame of reference are the laws of motion (mechanics) valid? Answer: In any frame of reference in uniform motion (the Principle of Galilean Relativity, from Lecture Three).

    C. Another simple question: In what frame of reference are the laws of electromagnetism (Maxwell's equations) valid?

        1. An equivalent question is "in what frame of reference does light go at speed c," or put another way, "relative to *what* does light go at speed c?"

        2. One possibility is that light goes at speed c relative to its source. This is ruled out by astronomical observations, especially of double-star systems.

        3. The nineteenth-century answer was that light goes at speed c relative to the *ether*, a hypothetical medium, or substance, believed to permeate the entire universe. The ether was thought to be the medium through which electromagnetic waves propagate, just as sound waves propagate through air and water waves, through water.

        4. Ether must have some unusual properties, being at once very stiff to account for the high speed of light, yet letting planets and other moving objects slip through without resistance and being able to permeate the tiniest of spaces.

        5. But to nineteenth-century physicists, ether's existence seemed essential.

III. A dichotomy in physics.

    A. One branch of physics, mechanics (or motion), obeys the relativity principle—meaning that the laws of mechanics are the same in all uniformly moving reference frames. As far as mechanics is concerned, the statement "I am moving" is meaningless; only relative motion matters.

B. The other branch of physics, electromagnetism, does not seem to obey the relativity principle.

1. This means that the laws of electromagnetism, including the prediction that electromagnetic waves move with speed *c*, are valid only in one frame of reference: the ether's frame.

2. As far as electromagnetism is concerned, the statement "I am moving" is meaningful and means "I am not at rest in the ether's frame of reference."

IV. An obvious question: Is Earth moving relative to the ether?

A. One possible answer is that it isn't, which leaves two possibilities:

1. Earth alone among all the universe is at rest with respect to the ether. This follows because all the other planets, stars, galaxies, and so on are moving relative to Earth. This possibility flies in the face of the Copernican notion that Earth isn't special; this idea is also ruled out by observational evidence.

2. Earth "drags" the ether in its local vicinity with it. The observed *aberration of starlight* rules this out. A good analogy is the example of using an umbrella to keep dry. If you run through the rain, then you need to hold the umbrella at an angle to keep dry. But if you "drag" the air in your vicinity with you, then the rain will fall vertically even if you run, and you won't need to tilt the umbrella. Similarly, because of Earth's motion around the Sun, a telescope will need to be pointed at different angles at different times of year to see the same star— provided Earth does not drag the ether with it. But if there is "ether drag," then the telescope angle will not need to be changed. In fact, the telescope angle must be changed—showing that Earth does not drag ether with it.

B. So Earth must be moving relative to the ether—and we should be able to detect that motion.

C. Where does this leave us?

    1. Air is not moving relative to the ether. By Copernican principles and sufficient observational evidence, we have to reject this.

    2. The Earth is dragging the ether with it. We have found that this is not true.

    3. Earth must be moving relative to the ether.

    4. We should, therefore, be able to detect the Earth's motion relative to the ether.

Essential Reading:

Hoffmann, *Relativity and Its Roots*, Chapter 4.

Hey and Walters, *Einstein's Mirror*, Chapter 2 through pp. 29–36.

Suggested Reading:

Einstein and Infeld, *The Evolution of Physics*, Chapter 3, through p. 160.

Questions to Consider:

1. You might be thinking "This ether sounds like a farfetched idea. Maybe it just doesn't exist." How, then, would you answer the question "with respect to what, does light go at speed *c*"?

2. Speculate on how the success of Newton's mechanical view of the universe led physicists to embrace the ether concept.

Aberration of Starlight: Umbrella Analogy

A) Standing Still. The man and the umbrella are both at rest with respect to the rain.

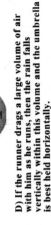

B) Running. Tilting the umbrella gives the best protection from the rain. Viewed from the frame of reference of the rain.

B) Running. Similar to B in all respects except viewed from the frame of reference of the running man.

D) If the runner drags a large volume of air with him as he runs, then the rain falls vertically within this volume and the umbrella is best held horizontally.

Lecture Five—Transcript
Speed c Relative to What?

Welcome to Lecture Five: "Speed c Relative to What?" with a big question mark after it. This is going to be a lecture full of questions, mostly questions about light and its behavior and, particularly, its speed c.

Before we get on to that, let me begin with a brief summary of where we've been before now—a brief history of physics through the year 1900. Because at this point we're at the jumping off place for the theory of relativity. We're at about the year 1900. Not quite. And we're ready to jump into relativity, and we have to put together where we've been. So here's a very brief history of physics through the year 1900.

In the years 1600 through 1750 we had Galileo, Newton, a lot of others developing an understanding of motion. Mechanics—the study of motion. They developed a mechanical understanding of physical reality. They could explain the way the world worked in terms of Newton's laws, gravity, and other forces and predict the motion of objects. They had a thorough understanding.

And I want to emphasize two aspects of the Galilean-Newtonian vision of reality that classical physics gave us. One is that the universe was deterministic. We're going to come back to that. We saw that in the clockwork universe. We'll come back to that when we get to quantum physics. The other thing was that a relativity principle holds in Newtonian and Galilean physics. The laws of Newtonian physics or Galilean physics work for any one in uniform motion. That's the principle of Galilean relativity. So, a relativity principle holds in this branch of physics.

Then, from roughly 1750 to about 1900, Maxwell and a whole host of others developed the theory of electromagnetism that I covered very briefly in the previous lecture. And that theory led to an understanding of all electromagnetic phenomena—electricity, magnetism, the interactions of the two, and especially light. Light was understood to be an electromagnetic wave. And Maxwell's equations made very definite predictions about those electromagnetic waves, specifically that they traveled at a known, calculatable speed—the speed of light, 186,000 miles a second, one foot per nanosecond, etc. So that's a brief history of physics to where we are about now.

And now we want to ask some questions about those two different branches of physics that are listed in that brief history. Mechanics—the study of motion—and the study of electricity and magnetism, including light.

Before we do I want to introduce a new concept. It's a concept called a *frame of reference*. What's a frame of reference? Well, you'd probably say it's something like your point of view. And in physics it is something like your point of view. It's basically sort of your state of motion; the things that share your state of motion.

If you're sitting here on Earth and you're doing physics experiments, Earth is your frame of reference. When you say, "I see a car moving at 50 miles an hour," you mean the car is moving at 50 miles an hour relative to the Earth and all the things that are attached to the Earth. If you're in an airplane flying at 600 miles an hour relative to Earth, the airplane is your frame of reference. And if you say, "I think I'll stroll down the aisle at 10 miles an hour," or something, that's relative to your frame of reference. Relative to the plane. If you're in a car moving down the highway and you want to do physics experiments in the car, the car is your frame of reference. Your frame of reference is basically the things that share your state of motion.

So that's the idea of a frame of reference. And I'm going to use that concept a lot in this and subsequent lectures. It's a crucial concept in relativity, because the relativity principle—Galilean or Einsteinian—is fundamentally about frames of reference.

So let's ask a very simple question. Let's ask the question in what frame of reference are the laws of mechanics, that is, the laws of motion, valid? In what frame of reference is this physics of the first half of our brief history of physics valid? We already know the answer to that question. We answered that question in lecture three with the Galilean relativity principle. The Galilean relativity principle said the laws of motion are the same for all observers in uniform motion. Put that in terms of frames of reference, it means the laws of physics, the laws of motion rather, the laws of mechanics, work equally well in all frames of reference in uniform motion.

So if I'm here on Earth, which, as I explained earlier, is a good enough approximation in uniform motion, or if I'm in that airplane moving through level air, no turbulence, at a steady speed, it's a valid frame of reference for doing mechanics of that frame of reference in which Newton's laws, the laws of mechanics, are valid. If I'm on Venus playing that tennis game, or even on that planet in that distant galaxy moving away from Earth at 0.8c, 80 percent of the speed of light—as long as that motion is uniform, that's still a valid frame of reference for doing mechanics. Newton's laws will be equally valid there. I'll do laboratory experiments. I'll verify Newton's laws. And those experiments will not be able to tell me I am or am not moving. That's a meaningless question as far as mechanics is concerned. That's what the mechanics principle of relativity, the Galilean relativity principle, means. It means that the answer to the question, in what frame of reference are the laws of mechanics valid? is in any uniformly moving frame of reference. Known for hundreds of years. Nothing special about that. But it's such a crucial question I want to emphasize it again. In what frame of reference are the laws of motion valid? Answer: in any uniformly moving frame of reference. It's an easy question to ask. It's an easy question to answer. And the essence of the answer is the Galilean principle of relativity that says the laws of physics are the same for everybody in uniform motion. Only it says the laws of motion, which was all the physics that was known in Galileo's time. And I want to emphasize that distinction. It's the laws of motion that are valid in all frames of reference. All uniformly moving frames of reference.

We now want to ask another question. Equally simple. In what frame of reference are Maxwell's equations valid? In what frame of reference are the laws of electromagnetism valid? In what frame of reference is that second part of physics valid? Is it valid in all frames of reference in uniform motion, like the laws of motion are? Or is there some special frame of reference in which the laws of electromagnetism are valid, and they're only valid in that frame? That's the question we want to concentrate on in this lecture. And that's a crucial question in the evolution of Einstein's thinking and relativity.

So, the question is, in what frame of reference are the laws of electromagnetism, Maxwell's equations that I displayed for you last time, in what frame of reference are they valid? Now that's actually not the question I'm going to ask. I'm going to ask an equivalent question. And I want you to understand why it's an equivalent question. I'm going to ask instead the question, in what frame of reference does light go at speed c? That special speed of 186,000 miles a second. In what frame of reference is it true that light goes at speed c? Why is that an equivalent question? Because one of the predictions of Maxwell's equations is that there should be electromagnetic waves, which we now know include light, and that those waves should travel at speed c. In a frame of reference in which Maxwell's equations are valid, that prediction will be borne out. It will be true. In a frame of reference in which Maxwell's equations are not valid, light will have a different speed. So the question, in what frame of reference does light go at speed c? is equivalent, logically equivalent, to the question, in what frame of reference are Maxwell's equations valid? We're going to ask that second question. In what frame of reference does light go at speed c?

Now, there's one easy possibility. You might say, well it's pretty obvious; it goes at speed c relative to its source. So if I have a light bulb and it's emitting light, then that light is traveling at speed c relative to the source of the light. And if I run with the source toward you, the light will be moving toward you faster than c, but it will be moving at speed c relative to the source.

Maybe Maxwell's equations apply to the source of light. That's a nice idea. It's not true. There's a lot of experimental confirmation that it's not true. But, perhaps, the easiest comes from observational evidence of double star systems. Astronomical observations of double star systems. About half the stars in our galaxy, it turns out, are double stars. There are two stars in close orbit or some orbit around each other like this. We don't happen to live in such a system or we'd have two suns.

So, here's a double star system. And it's going around like this. Two stars are going around each other. Now notice what's going on. Here's a time when this yellow star is coming toward you. Here's a time when this yellow star is going away from you. Now this star system may be a long ways away from us, thousands of light years or something, that means light takes thousands of years to get from it to us. If the speed of light depended on the speed of the source, the light leaving the yellow star when it's coming toward us is going to get to us a lot sooner than the light leaving the yellow star when it's going away from us. We may even see several images of the star as light from different positions arrives at the same time, because it took different amounts of time to travel and the star was in different places at different times. We certainly won't see this nice, simple motion, which, after all, is what Newton's law of gravity predicts. If the speed of light depended on the speed of the source, we would see very strange things with double star systems. We would be able to interpret what that double star system was actually doing—a nice, simple orbit—but we wouldn't see that.

Well, the fact is, when we look at double star systems, it's very, very clear that the speed of the light coming from the stars has no relation to the speed of the source. The light comes by us at speed c, regardless of what the source is moving. So, unfortunately, the simple answer, that light goes at speed c relative to the source is plain and simple wrong.

Now, in the nineteenth century, physicists gave a different answer to that question. They looked at other kinds of waves they knew about. Sound waves. They traveled about 700 miles an hour. With respect to what? With respect to the air. Because sound waves are disturbances of air. Earthquake waves travel through the solid Earth at speeds of several miles a second or more. Relative to what? Relative to the solid Earth, which is the thing which is being disturbed by the passage of those waves. Ocean waves travel along the ocean surface at characteristic speeds that depend, in the case of ocean waves, on how big the waves are. That makes them more complicated than electromagnetic waves by the way. But what determines that, what is that speed measured relative to? It's measured relative to the water. If the waves were in a flowing river, relative to the bank they would have the river speed added to the wave speed. It's very clear what the speed of a wave means when it's a wave that's a disturbance of the air, like a sound wave, or a disturbance of the water surface like an ocean wave, or a disturbance of the solid Earth like an earthquake wave.

Well, nineteenth century physicists were first of all very thrilled with the success of Newtonian physics in explaining everything in mechanical terms. And they were still trying to think about electromagnetism as if it were mechanical. They were trying to think of light waves as being very much like sound waves—mechanical disturbances of some medium. So, they came up with the idea of a hypothetical
medium. Medium being like the air or the water, the thing that the

wave is traveling through that it's a disturbance of. And they called it the *ether*.

And the ether had to have unusual properties. It permeated all of space, because light waves, after all, travel in the so-called vacuum of empty space—for example, between the Earth and the moon, or the Earth and the sun. Sound waves don't travel there. Water waves don't travel there. There's no air. There's no water there. Earthquake waves—there's no Earth. But light waves do travel there. Electromagnetic waves. Radio waves. They travel through empty space, or seemingly empty space.

So the ether had to pervade all space. It got into the tiniest interstices of empty space, because we know that light travels in little vacuums we make in vacuum tubes and things like that. Light goes everywhere—at least if the material isn't opaque. So the ether had to be very able to get everywhere. It also had to be very tenuous, because, after all, the Earth goes around its orbit and has been doing so for billions of years, and it isn't feeling any drag, like a satellite does when we launch it in too low an orbit, and it feels drag from the Earth's atmosphere, and eventually spirals into the atmosphere, and crashes to Earth or burns up. Earth hasn't done that with respect to the sun. And it would if the ether presented much resistance. So, it had to be very tenuous.

Furthermore, it has to be very stiff, for a reason that's a little bit more subtle. It turns out, if you send a wave down something like a stretched string, a stretch of string, and wiggle it and send a wave down it, you'll find the wave goes faster if the string is stretched tighter. So the ether, to propagate waves, move waves at a very, very rapid speed of 186,000 miles a second, had to be very stiff. A property that's not really very compatible with being very tenuous. So, it was a strange substance that physicists of the nineteenth century proposed. But it seemed essential to those physicists, because they were steeped in this mechanical view.

Now, if you're saying to yourself, "Wait, this is a preposterous substance. Why on Earth did they make this? Why didn't they just say light waves go through empty space?" Well, if you say that, then you're back to the question, with respect to what does light go at speed *c*? Because empty space isn't a something, like a substance is. If I say, light goes at speed *c* relative to the ether, it's clear what I mean. But if I say, it goes at speed *c* relative to empty space; it's not clear what that means. And you're left with a deep philosophical question about your fundamental ideas of physics.

So, we're going to pursue the nineteenth century answer for a little while. The answer is light goes at speed c relative to this hypothetical substance—the ether. Now, there's a philosophical problem here if you accept this ether idea, and it rises in the form of a dichotomy in the two branches of physics I've just been describing. I've talked about the study of motion and how in the study of motion a relativity principle holds. The laws of motion are the same for anybody who cares to study them, as long as that individual is in uniform motion. There is no one special frame of reference where the laws of mechanics, the laws of motion, are valid. A relativity principle holds.

But now we've asked the question for electromagnetism, we said, in what frame of reference does light go at speed c? I argued that that was equivalent to saying, "In what frame of reference are the laws of Maxwell, the laws of electromagnetism, valid?" And the answer is: They're valid in this one special frame of reference, a frame of reference at rest with respect to the ether. So we have a dichotomy. One branch of physics obeys a relativity principle and the other doesn't. And that is, to say the least, philosophically unsatisfying. But I urge you to think about the alternative, and you'll quickly get mired in greater philosophical difficulties.

So that was where things stood in the nineteenth century. We have this dichotomy. Physicists believed that the laws of electromagnetism were valid in one special frame of reference, that the statement "I am moving" is meaning*ful* in electromagnetism. I am moving means I am moving with respect to the ether. Whereas, "I am moving" is a meaningless statement in mechanics. That means we ought to be able to do physical experiments involving electromagnetism that will tell us whether we're moving or not.

Now, remember back to the first lecture when I had you playing tennis. You played tennis on a cruise ship, on Venus, on this distant planet moving away from Earth at 80 percent of the speed of light. And you had no problem with that. Maybe you had a little more problem with the second thing I asked you to do, or it was a little more obscure. And that was heat a cup of tea in a microwave oven. That involved electromagnetism. That's why I had you do that. And if you were a believer in the status of these two branches of physics, as they were at the end of the nineteenth century, you would have told me, yes, I can play tennis on this distant planet moving at 80 percent of the speed of light, and it worked just the same as it does on Earth, because the relativity principle holds for the laws of motion. But you would say, no, the microwave oven isn't going to work at all. The microwaves really are going to get crashed to one side of the oven or left behind or something, because that oven is moving at 80 percent of the speed of light relative to Earth. And the laws of electromagnetism seem to work pretty well on Earth.

So, we have this dichotomy in physics. However, we're going to plow ahead with the philosophically unsatisfying dichotomy. We're going to ask another question. We're going to ask: Okay, there is this ether-like substance, how is Earth moving relative to the ether? Because if the ether exists, Earth must either be moving through it or not moving through it. And I want to take you through some important logic. And this logic is crucial, because if you follow this logic, you will be forced to believe in relativity when we get there. We're not there yet, but we will be soon, and you'll be forced to believe in it. Logically, you'll understand why it must be.

So, let's look a little bit at the question, Is Earth moving relative to ether? And there are really two possibilities. One possibility is that it isn't moving relative to the ether. If it isn't moving relative to the ether, then one possibility is Earth alone, among all the cosmos, is at rest relative to the ether. Now, that may be an absurd possibility, but maybe it's true. Or possibly the Earth is at rest relative to the ether because the ether that's locally in Earth's vicinity gets dragged along with it. Well, let's look at these two possibilities.

I think you can see that the first one probably isn't going to be very philosophically satisfying, regardless of its physical content—it isn't satisfying physically either because it violates the Copernican principle that the Earth isn't special.

Let's look at the second one in some degree of detail. Possibly the Earth drags the ether in its vicinity with it, and if the Earth does what Mars does too, and what Venus does, and that distant planet, and everybody sees themselves at rest with respect to the ether, even though the different ether is moving with respect to them, how could we find out if that's true or not? Of course, the other possibility is the Earth is moving relative to the ether. So we want to rule out the first possibility, if we can, or rule out the second possibility.

So, let's look at the two sub-possibilities—the possibility that the Earth drags the ether with it in its vicinity. Fortunately, there's an astronomical observation we can make that will answer this question of whether the Earth drags the ether in its vicinity with it, and presumably then whether the other planets and stars and astronomical objects do that as well. The phenomenon is called the *aberration of starlight* and it involves the question of whether we have to look in different directions to see the same star if we look at it at different times of year. Why would that happen? Why would we have to look in different directions? Well, it has to do with the motion of the Earth in relation to the motion of the light coming from the star. And the best way to explain that to you is to give you an analogy involving an umbrella.

So here's the analogy. Suppose it's raining, and raining vertically downward, and I want to keep dry. How do I do it? I put an umbrella directly over my head. I'm standing still in vertically falling rain and I want to keep driest; I put an umbrella directly over my head. There I go. I stay nice and dry. That's great.

But now what happens if I want to move somewhere—I want to run through the rain or walk rapidly through the rain. What should I do with the umbrella? Should I continue to hold it right over my head so it will keep my head dry, or should I do something different? Well, I'm going to convince you that you should do something different. Here's what happens if I run through the rain. I would argue that I have to tilt the umbrella at an angle. That angle is going to depend on how fast I'm moving relative to how fast the rain is falling. I'm going to have to tilt at an angle toward the direction I'm moving in order to stay driest.

Why does that work? Well, it works; you can understand that by looking at what the situation looks like in my frame of reference. Right now we're looking at a situation, first where I stood still, then if I run, but I'm still drawing that picture from the Earth's frame of reference, and I'm moving past the Earth and the rain is falling vertically. But in my frame of reference, it looks different. As I move toward the falling rain, the rain looks to me like it's coming at an angle. And that's the angle I have to tilt my umbrella at. And, again, that angle depends on basically how fast I'm moving relative to how fast the rain is falling. So, I've got to tilt my umbrella to stay dry. So here it goes. It's raining. I want to get from here to there. To do so, I tilt the umbrella. I tilt it at an angle that depends on how fast I'm going. If I'm walking slowly, maybe it's like that. If I'm running a bit faster, maybe it's more like that. And you might say, "How can that be? His head is exposed." Well, the rain that was going to hit my head is long passed by the time it gets there. The other rain has been intercepted by the umbrella. Rain that would have hit my head when I had reached this point has already hit the umbrella and has avoided me. So, I actually do stay driest if I tilt the umbrella in the direction I'm going, at a tilt angle that depends on how fast I'm moving relative to the falling rain.

Well, that's all well and good. But what happens if instead I drag some big volume of air with me? That would be analogous to the Earth dragging the ether with it—Mars, Venus, all the other astronomical objects dragging the ether with them. What happens if they do drag the ether with them? What happens to the angle I have to tilt a telescope to look at a star? What happens to the angle I have to tilt my umbrella if a large volume of air comes along with me? Actually, some volume of air actually does come along with me as I walk through the air. There's a small volume right next to my skin that isn't moving. It's been caught by my skin, and it moves along with me. But it's only a tiny, tiny fraction of a millimeter. So that's not important. But what if instead I drag a big volume of air, several times my size, big enough so that if the rain falls vertically in the air above that isn't moving with me, it gets into the air that is moving with me, it has time to get sped up by the motion of that air until it's moving along with me. What happens then? Well, the rain is going to fall. It's going to suddenly hit this volume of air that's moving with me. Temporarily, it's not going to be moving at that rate. But, it's going to feel a wind like force on it. It's going to speed up. Eventually, it's going to be moving with me. And then relative to me, it's going to be falling vertically. Relative to somebody standing still on Earth, it's going to now be moving at an angle within that huge blob of air.

Let's take a look at what that would look like. So, here I am. I'm running along. I've got this big volume of air I'm dragging with me. The rain is falling in my frame of reference at what looks like an angle. But once it gets into this blob of air, it's moving along with me, horizontally. And so it falls vertically again, and I do not need to change the angle at which I tilt my umbrella. So, if in fact I drag a big volume of air with me, then I walk along, don't tilt my umbrella. I walk in a different direction, I don't tilt my umbrella. Everything is fine.

How can I tell if I drag a volume of air with me? Simple. I do this experiment. I ask myself, "How do I stay driest?" I ask myself, "At what angle do I need to point my umbrella to stay driest?" If the answer is: I need to point it at some angle, and that angle changes if I change direction, because I always want to point it in the direction I'm going, then I've got good evidence that I don't drag a big volume of air with me.

On the other hand, as I move around, no matter which direction I'm going, I find I just hold the umbrella vertically and that will keep me driest. Then I conclude that I move a big volume of air with me, I drag a big volume of air with me.

Well, that's an analogy for this phenomenon of aberration of starlight that I mentioned. In the analogy, the umbrella becomes a telescope. We're going to look at a distant star with a telescope. So let me get a telescope. We're going to ask the question, do I need to point the telescope in different directions? Just like, did I need to tilt the umbrella? So what corresponds to the rain? Well, it's the thing that was falling in that case. Here, it's the thing that's coming to us from the star, namely, the starlight. So, in order to see the star, do I have to point the telescope in different directions depending on how I'm moving?

Now, I'm not going to run around the Earth with a big telescope. I couldn't run fast enough anyway. But what I am going to do is take account of the fact that the Earth, in its orbital motion, moves about 20 miles a second. So, at one time of year it's moving 20 miles a second this way. But we're in a circular orbit around the sun. So, six months later, I'm moving 20 miles a second in a different direction. And it's very much like the umbrella. Again, when I moved in this direction, if I wasn't dragging the air with me, I tilted the umbrella like this. When I get to the other end of the room here, and I want to go back, I don't simply hold the umbrella like that. That'd get me very wet. Instead, I tilt the umbrella in the other direction. So I'm still pointing it in the direction of my motion. And then I stay driest. The important point here is not so much the angle I had to tilt it at. The actual angle would be hard to measure accurately with starlight. What's important is the fact that if I move in a different direction,

I've got to shift the actual direction the umbrella is pointing so that it's always going in the direction I'm moving. That's the crucial point.

So, if we go to the analogy again, that means if I look at the star at one time of year, and I point it in this direction, if I find out that six months later I have to switch the direction of the telescope, that is, it's still pointing at an angle, but before it was pointing this way, now it's pointing this way, then I conclude that aberration of starlight is occurring. The apparent position of the star is changing. And I conclude I don't drag a big volume of, not air but in this case in the analogy, ether, with me. So that is the phenomenon of aberration of starlight. And we can actually do that experiment.

Now remember what determined that angle. The angle in the umbrella case depended on how fast I was running relative to how fast the rain was falling. What's the analogy in the astronomical case? What's the analogy that gives me the angle at which I tilt the telescope? It's a question of how fast the Earth is moving, in its orbital motion relative to the speed of the stuff that's coming down from the star, namely, the speed of light. Well, the speed of light is a big speed. It's 186,000 miles a second. We don't know the absolute speed of the Earth relative to the ether, but we do know that it changes by about 40 miles a second, because one time we're going 40 miles a second this way, and six months later we're going 40 miles a second the other way. So, the change in angle is going to be a very small change, something like the ratio of 40 miles a second to 186,000 miles a second. It's going to be a tiny angle.

But we can measure it with astronomical telescopes, because what we do is take a picture of a field of stars. And we look at the positions of the stars on a photographic plate—or more currently on an electronic detector—and we see if those positions change with time of year. And we can measure that angle. And what happens when we do that experiment? What happens is we find that the positions do, indeed, shift or, equivalently, to get the star exactly the same place on our photographic plate, we have to tilt the telescope at a different angle; aberration of starlight occurs.

Back to our full picture here of the aberration of starlight problem. The analogy with the umbrella, we see that that rules out the possibility that we drag a big volume of the ether with us. So the

Earth does not drag the ether with us. And that aberration of starlight is a convincing demonstration of that. So where does this leave us?

Let's go back to the logic we were talking about before. We had two possibilities. We asked the question: Is the Earth moving relative to the ether? One possibility, it isn't. The other possibility, it is. We want to rule out one of those two possibilities. Well, I think philosophical grounds alone are sufficient to rule out the idea that Earth, of all the things in the universe—Mars, Jupiter, Venus, the sun, the center of our galaxy, that planet in that distant galaxy moving away from us at 80 percent of the speed of light—that all those things are in motion relative to ether but Earth is not. That as Earth goes around the sun in its orbit, the entire ether throughout the whole universe moves to partake of that motion and keep Earth at rest relative to the ether. That's nonsense. That violates everything Copernicus was trying to tell us—that the Earth is not special, the Earth is not the center of things. Furthermore, if you don't like that philosophical argument for ruling out that possibility, there's plenty of observational evidence, from astronomy particularly, that rules out the possibility that Earth alone, amongst everything, is at rest relative to the ether. Just isn't true.

So, then there was the other possibility that would allow us to conclude that the Earth isn't moving relative to the ether. And that would be if the Earth drags the ether in its vicinity with it, and the aberration of starlight observations allow us to conclude that that isn't the case. And, therefore, we have ruled out entirely the first possibility—that the Earth is not moving relative to the ether. It must be moving, relative to the ether. The second possibility is the case. And if it is moving relative to the ether, then there must be a wind of ether blowing past the Earth, because the Earth is moving relative to the ether. The ether, alternatively, is blowing past the Earth, just like if you stick your arm out the window of a moving car. Even on a calm day, you feel a wind. It's the wind, the apparent wind, caused by your motion through the air. Similarly, the Earth's motion through the ether should give rise to a wind of ether blowing past the Earth.

We should be able to determine the speed and direction of that wind. Why? Because we have a branch of physics, which is valid only in a frame of reference at rest with respect to the ether and will give different answers in a different frame of reference. And, in particular,

　　　©2000 The Teaching Company Limited Partnership

will give different answers depending on how we're moving relative to the ether. So, we should be able to design an experiment that tries to answer the—we know logically, we've ruled out the possibility that we're not moving relative to the ether. We are moving relative to the ether. And we should, therefore, be able to devise some kind of experiment, if it's sensitive enough, that detects Earth's motion relative to ether and answers two questions: How fast are we moving relative to the ether? And in what direction?

It's going to have to be a sensitive experiment, because it's going to involve questions of the Earth's speed in relation to the speed of light, because we're going to ask electromagnetic questions. And we can't answer this question with mechanics, because in mechanics there's a relativity principle, and all frames of reference that are uniformly moving are equivalent. But we can answer it with electromagnetism, because we had this dichotomy. And at the end of the nineteenth century, physicists believed that the principles of electromagnetism were valid only in one frame of reference, the ether frame of reference. We've ruled out Earth being at rest in the ether frame of reference. Earth is, therefore, moving relative to that frame. And we're now going to set out and try to detect that motion. And one of the most famous and important experiments in all of physics did precisely that. And it's the experiment I'll be describing in the next lecture.

Lecture Six
Earth and the Ether: A Crisis in Physics

Scope:

Forced to the conclusion that Earth must be moving through the ether, physicists set out to detect and measure that motion. From our perspective on Earth, our motion through the ether should manifest itself as an "ether wind." As a result of that wind, the speed of light should be different in different directions. In the 1880s, the American physicists Albert Michelson and Edward Morley conceived an experiment to detect the ether wind and answer the question "How is Earth moving relative to the ether?" Their experiment compared the travel times for light following two mutually perpendicular paths. It used interference of light to make a very precise comparison of the two travel times and was sensitive enough to detect motion much slower than that of Earth in its orbit around the Sun. Thus, the Michelson-Morley experiment could definitely determine Earth's motion through the ether. But the experiment failed to detect any such motion! This failure left physics with a deep contradiction: Having already ruled out the possibility that Earth is at rest with respect to the ether, the Michelson-Morley experiment now showed that Earth is not moving with respect to the ether. Physicists proposed a number of ad hoc explanations for the Michelson-Morley result, but none had any sound theoretical basis.

Outline

I. We have been forced to the conclusion that Earth must be moving relative to the ether.

   A. Equivalently, there should be an "ether wind" blowing past Earth, and we should be able to measure the speed and direction of that wind.

   B. Specifically, the speed of light should be different in different directions, depending on whether the light is traveling with or against the ether wind—just as the speed of sound is different, depending on whether the sound is moving with or against the wind.

II. The Michelson-Morley experiment.

  A. In the 1880s, Michelson and Morley designed an experiment to detect Earth's motion through the ether. By 1887, their apparatus was far more sensitive than needed to measure a speed comparable to that of Earth in its orbit around the Sun.

  B. The Michelson-Morley experiment used an ingenious system of mirrors to compare the speeds of light in two perpendicular directions. It takes longer to row a boat a given distance up a river and back than it does to row the same distance across the river and back. Similarly, it should take light different times to make a round trip of the same length parallel and perpendicular to the ether wind. The Michelson-Morley experiment sought to detect this difference.

  1. The extreme sensitivity of the experiment resulted from its use of *interference* between the two light beams. The experiment did not actually measure speeds for the light beams, but rather was sensitive to *differences* in speed.

  2. Michelson and Morley performed their experiment with the apparatus in many different orientations. They also performed it at different times of year, corresponding to different directions of Earth's orbital motion (relative to the hypothetical "ether wind").

  C. There was never any change in the interference pattern— meaning that Michelson and Morley could not detect any motion of Earth through the ether.

III. This "null result" gave rise to a serious contradiction.

  A. The Copernican paradigm and astronomical observations (especially aberration of starlight) rule out Earth's being at rest with respect to the ether.

  B. The Michelson-Morley experiment appears to rule out Earth's moving with respect to the ether.

  C. In attempts to salvage the ether concept, the Irish physicist George Fitzgerald and the Dutch physicist Hendrik Lorentz independently proposed that objects shrink in the direction of their motion through the ether.

1. This shrinkage was such that the Michelson-Morley light path parallel to the ether wind would be shorter by just the right amount to keep the travel time for the two perpendicular light beams the same—ensuring that the experiment could never detect motion through the ether.

2. The Lorentz-Fitzgerald proposition had no physical or conceptual justification whatsoever; it was just an ad hoc assumption designed to explain away the Michelson-Morley result.

Essential Reading:

Hoffmann, *Relativity and Its Roots*, Chapter 4, pp. 75–80.

Hey and Walters, *Einstein's Mirror*, Chapter 2, pp. 38–45.

Suggested Reading:

Einstein and Infeld, *The Evolution of Physics*, Chapter 3, pp. 160–186.

Questions to Consider:

1. Did the Michelson-Morley experiment actually determine values for the speed of light in two different directions? If not, what did it measure?

2. Why was it necessary to repeat the Michelson-Morley experiment at different times of the year and with the apparatus in different orientations?

3. It is not necessary for the two arms of the Michelson-Morley apparatus to be the same length. Why not?

Wave Speed Depends on the Wind Speed and Direction

The air (represented by the gray square) is at rest relative to the viewer. The sound waves move toward the viewer at a speed of 700 mph relative to the air *and* the viewer.

The air moves toward the viewer at a speed of 50 mph. The sound, traveling through the medium of the air, is thus moving toward the viewer with a speed of 750 mph.

The air moves away from the viewer at a speed of 50 mph. The sound, traveling through the medium of the air, is thus moving toward the viewer at the reduced speed of 650 mph.

The Michelson-Morley Experiment

The Michelson-Morley experiment was an ingenious device for detecting the movement of an hypothesized "ether" medium with respect to the earth. With this elaborate device, a single beam of light (1), emanating from the light source (far left), is split by a beam splitter (center) into two beams (2 and 3) and through the use of mirrors (top and far right) is recombined into a single beam (4 and 5) aimed at a viewer (bottom).

The experiment relies not on precision timing of the separate light beams, but rather on the interference pattern created by the recombined light.

Wave Interference

Michelson-Morley Apparatus

The resulting interference pattern

Wave interference, caused by two or more different waves combining, can have several possible outcomes, two of which are pictured here. In A, two light waves combine with wave troughs and wave crests coinciding, resulting in a wave with a higher amplitude. This is called **Constructive Interference**. In B, two light waves combine with troughs in the upper wave coinciding with wave crests in the bottom wave, resulting in a cancellation of the wave. This is called **Destructive Interference**.

Lecture Six—Transcript
Earth and the Ether: A Crisis in Physics

In the previous lecture we asked the question: In what frame of reference are the laws of motion valid? And we gave the same answer we gave back in Lecture Three. And the same answer you realized was true in Lecture One, namely, they're valid for anybody in uniform motion.

Then we went on and asked a similar question for the laws of electromagnetism that we had just learned about, including their prediction that there were electromagnetic waves, and the electromagnetic waves moved at a certain speed, the speed c, the speed of light. So we asked the question: In what frame of reference are those laws valid? We found that was equivalent to the question: With respect to what does light go at speed c? And then, I introduced the nineteenth century answer to that question—with respect to the ether, a hypothetical medium that permeated all of the universe and was the medium in which light waves are a disturbance. Similarly to the way that the air is the medium in which sound waves here on Earth are a disturbance, or the ocean is the medium in which water waves are a disturbance.

And then we asked the logical question: How is Earth moving relative to the ether? And we've been through a series of very rigorous, logical steps in an attempt to answer that question. And we're partway there now, and we're going to continue that logic today. And I want to do this with considerable rigor. Because at the end of today's lecture, we're going to be in real crisis in physics, and I want you to understand how we got to that crisis and how difficult it's going to be to get out of it.

So, let me just review briefly the logic that got us to where we are now. We asked the question: Is Earth moving relative to the ether? There are two possibilities. Either it isn't, or it is. We looked last time in considerable detail at the possibility that it isn't moving relative to the ether. There were two possibilities then. Either Earth alone among everything in the cosmos was at rest relative to the ether. That's an absurd conclusion given the Copernican principle that the Earth is not a special place in the universe. It's particularly absurd in light of what we know from modern cosmology, namely, that there are places in the universe, distant galaxies in particular, that are moving away from us at speeds that are very close to the speed of light—80, 90 percent of the speed of light. It's absurd to imagine that everything in the universe is pinned to the Earth, when there's such a wide range of speeds relative to Earth throughout the universe. So, we've ruled out the first possibility, that Earth alone among everything in the universe is at rest with respect to the ether. We ruled that out, basically, philosophically, on Copernican grounds. I also guarantee you, it's also ruled out on grounds from observational astronomy and other measurements we can make. But it suffices to rule it out on this philosophical ground.

The second possibility was that the Earth drags the ether in its immediate vicinity with it. And, presumably, so do all the other astronomical bodies. We looked at the possibility that that was true. I gave you an example involving an umbrella and trying to keep dry in the rain as I moved through the rain. Analogous to the Earth moving through the ether and having to point a telescope in different directions. And astronomical observations convince us, on that basis, that the Earth does not drag the ether in its immediate vicinity with us. So, we've ruled out that possibility as well. Together then, we've ruled out the possibility that the Earth is not moving relative to the ether.

So we're forced to the logical conclusion that the Earth must be moving relative to the ether. If it is moving relative to the ether, then just as a rider in a convertible car is feeling a wind going past them, even though the air may be still because of the motion of the car, similarly, if Earth is moving through the ether, there must be an ether wind blowing past the Earth. And we ought to be able to detect that wind somehow. We can't detect it by a mechanical means, by the laws of motion, because, you know, they're the same in all frames of reference. They don't care about the motion of ether. But we should be able to detect it with some kind of electromagnetic experiment. Some kind of experiment involving electricity and magnetism. Because we believe in the ether paradigm that the laws of electricity and magnetism are valid exactly only in the ether's frame of reference, and if we're moving relative to ether, we should be able to detect some subtle differences.

So, the other possibility is that the Earth is moving relative to the ether. That's the only possibility we have left. And if that's true, there must be this ether wind blowing past Earth. We should be able to detect that ether wind, and, in particular, to measure both its speed and direction. And that's what we want to try to do.

Let me carry this a little bit further and suggest how we might do that. If you have a wave of any kind, and let me talk first about a sound wave here in air. If you have a wave that travels at a certain speed with respect to that, to its medium, in the case of a sound wave, that medium is air. Sound waves go about 700 miles an hour with respect to air. That's, incidentally, why jet planes travel no more than about 600 or so miles an hour, because they don't want to go supersonic. It requires a whole different engineering to do that. So that kind of sets an upper limit to the speed of everyday airplanes.

The speed of sound is about, anyway, 700 miles an hour, about a thousand feet per second. That's why when you hear, when you see lightening and count the seconds until thunder, every five seconds represents about a mile—because the speed of light is almost instantaneous, and the speed of sound is about a thousand feet a second. Anyway, the speed of sound is about 700 miles an hour. If there's a wind blowing at, say, 50 miles an hour in the direction the sound waves are going, the sound waves will be going relative to the Earth and relative to you, if you're standing still on Earth, at 750 miles an hour.

So what's that look like? The wave speed—that's the important point—the speed of these sound waves, depends on the wind speed and on the direction of the wind. I'm showing a picture here, which shows you standing at rest on Earth. A blob of, at this point, air surrounds you. And the air is at rest. And there is a series of sound waves coming at you at 700 miles an hour relative to the air. And they're also moving at 700 miles an hour relative to you, because the air is at rest relative to you. The speed of sound is 700 miles an hour relative to the air. The air is not moving with respect to you. Therefore, this sound is going 700 miles an hour with respect to you.

If, on the other hand, the wind is blowing toward you, and I've put a little arrow here on the blob of air to represent the fact that the whole air is moving, the air is carrying the sound waves. The sound waves are moving at 700 miles an hour relative to the air. Let's say the wind is blowing at 50 miles an hour. Then the sound waves are coming at 750 miles an hour relative to you. So that the wave speed that you measure, the speed of sound that you measure, is different than it would be if there weren't a wind blowing. In this case, with the wind blowing in the direction the sound waves are moving toward you, you will get a speed that is greater—750 miles an hour.

If, on the other hand, the wind is blowing away from you but the sound is still coming toward you, then the speed of sound will be reduced for you. It's still 700 miles an hour relative to the air, but because the air is blowing away from you at, say, 50 miles an hour, the sound waves are going past you at only 650 miles an hour. So, the wave speed depends on the wind speed and the direction.

Incidentally, you might speculate about what would happen if the wind speed were exactly the speed of sound. Those sound waves would never get to you.

Well, let's re-do this example. But now, let's talk about light and the ether. If we talk about light and the ether, my blob of air, the medium in which sound waves propagate, now represents the ether. The sound waves now become light waves. Light waves travel at a known speed—the speed c, 186,000 miles a second, 300,000 kilometers a second, one foot per nanosecond—relative to the ether. That's the nineteenth century hypothesis. So, if we're at rest with respect to the ether, we will measure c for the speed of sound. And we will measure c for the speed of sound no matter which—or speed of light rather—we will measure c for the speed of light. And we'll measure c for the speed of light, no matter which way the light is moving, because the ether is still with respect to us.

But we've ruled out the possibility that the ether is at rest with respect to Earth, or Earth is at rest with respect to the ether. We know the ether must be moving with respect to Earth or Earth is moving through the ether. There must, therefore, be an ether wind blowing past the Earth. And therefore, in some directions, depending on whether light is moving with the ether wind or against the ether wind, or maybe sideways to the ether wind, the speed of light should have different values. And if we could build a sensitive enough experiment and send light in different directions, we should be able to detect that difference. And we should be able to use that difference to
calculate the speed of the Earth and the direction of the Earth relative to the ether. That's the experiment physicists wanted to do in the nineteenth century.

There were a number of attempts to do that experiment. Early attempts failed, for a number of reasons—some of them fairly theoretical and some of them because they simply weren't sensitive enough. The problem is, we already know that even though Earth must be moving relative to the ether—that's what our logic told us— that motion can't be very, very fast. If that motion were, say, 90 percent of the speed of light, it would be very obvious to us that Maxwell's laws of electromagnetism worked differently in some directions than others. It would be very obvious that the speed of light was different in different directions.

If we are moving relative to the ether, which logic tells us we are, that motion is not real fast, compared to the speed of light. That already should raise up your hackles a little bit. Because if there are people out there on planets or in distant galaxies moving away from us at 80 percent of the speed of light, they must be moving pretty fast relative to the ether. Because, remember, they don't drag the ether with them. But we are moving relatively slowly compared to the ether, and we want to find out just how fast that is.

We can't move very fast at all on Earth relative to the speed of light. But we do have a faster speed available to us, and that's the speed of the Earth in its orbit around the sun. As I mentioned before, that speed is about 20 miles a second.

Now, we don't know how fast the whole sun and the solar system are moving relative to the ether. But we do know this: We do know that at one point in the year, if we're moving at 20 miles a second this way, six months later we're moving at 20 miles a second the other way. And that's a difference in speed of 40 miles a second—from going 20 miles a second this way, to 20 miles a second that way. And we have that difference in speeds to play with. And 20 miles a second is not big compared to the speed of light. But at least it's not absolutely negligible.

By the way, for you mathematically inclined types, these experiments depend not on the ratio of the speed of the object through the ether, to the speed of light, but on the square of that ratio, which is an even smaller number. Take 20 miles a second, or 40 miles a second, over 186,000 miles a second. That's a tiny number. Square it, it's even smaller. So these experiments have to be very sensitive.

I'm not going to describe the earlier attempts. But I'm going to describe in some detail the attempt that was carried out in the 1880s by the American physicists Michelson and Morley at Case Institute in Cleveland, Ohio. And this was an experiment they started in the early 1880s. By 1887, the experiment was sensitive enough to detect motion 10 times slower than the known motion of the Earth in its orbit. So it was clearly sensitive enough to detect the motion of the Earth through the ether. No question about that at all. I want to spend a good bit of time describing this experiment, because it really locks us into this crisis we're going to get to by the end of this lecture.

So let's take a look at the Michelson-Morley apparatus. The Michelson-Morley experiment consists, schematically, of several parts. It has a light source. It has two mirrors. It has a viewer. And it has a device called a beam splitter. And the beam splitter is nothing but a lousy mirror. It's a piece of glass that has had silver coated on it or aluminum coated on it, but not thick enough to make it a really good mirror. It reflects about half the light that hits it. But about half the light gets through. Today, we use slightly more sophisticated devices. But that was what was used in Michelson-Morley's day. And it works quite satisfactorily. So the beam splitter, think of it as a mirror—half the light that hits that mirror goes through and half the light is reflected.

So let's see what happens when we turn on the light source in the Michelson-Morley apparatus and send a light beam out. Out comes the light beam and it hits the half-silvered mirror. Some of it goes straight through and hits a distant mirror. Some of it reflects off the half silvered mirror, bends at a right angle, because the mirror is placed diagonally, and hits another mirror.

So, what we've established here are basically two arms. There's a path from the half-silvered mirror to the upper mirror, and there's a path for light to travel horizontally from the half-silvered mirror to the right hand mirror. The light has been split, and it's going to travel on two different paths. It then bounces off these flat mirrors and comes back. So, back comes one light beam. Back comes the other light beam. They join at the half-silvered mirror. Some of the light goes straight through, some of the light is reflected in each case, and the important point is, there is light that's been recombined. The original light left the source, traveled to the half-silvered mirror, split into two beams that went out in two mutually perpendicular directions, came back and joined, and goes into a viewer. This is the experiment with which we're going to try to detect Earth's motion through the ether.

How are we going to do it? Well, we have in this Michelson-Morley apparatus these two paths for the light to travel. These two arms. The one that goes vertically, the one, in this case, that goes horizontally, although the whole apparatus was actually laid out horizontally on the ground.

Let me just give you a little historical description of this apparatus before I go on. We can, today, build something that looks very much like this on an optical table, which is just a big, heavy hunk of metal that doesn't vibrate much. About this big. And we can build this apparatus and pretty much carry out an experiment like this using lasers and modern optical components. Michelson and Morley couldn't do that. They actually floated their apparatus on a 13-foot diameter slab of stone floating in liquid mercury. Sensitive optical experiments have to be isolated from vibration. And it took a lot of effort to do that. And, furthermore, they had lots of mirrors, and the light bounced back and forth many times to make the light paths longer. But in principle, this is what the apparatus looked like.

What we're going to try to do is detect differences in the travel time for the light on these two paths. For now, think of those two paths as being identical in length—but I'm going to assure you that isn't at all crucial, and I'll show you why in just a minute.

Now, it's not good enough simply to time the travel time of the light and the two paths with a stopwatch. We just don't have stopwatches accurate enough. We couldn't even do that—well, in today's technology, we might just barely be able to actually time the travel time. But in the 1800s that was impossible. Instead, Michelson and Morley used a much cleverer and more sensitive method to try to detect a difference in travel time for the two light paths. They weren't concerned about the actual value of the speed of light in two different directions. That didn't matter. All that mattered was whether the speed of light was different in two different directions. That's enough, knowing how different it is and knowing the different directions, to tell you something about the speed of the Earth relative to the ether.

Why do you expect a difference in travel time? Suppose there's an ether wind blowing in this apparatus. Suppose the wind is blowing horizontally, from right to left, for example. I assert that it will take light longer to travel up this path and back than it will to travel along this path and back at right angles to the wind. You might say, well, why is that. Why should it take any longer to travel upstream and back?

Think about a boat rowing in a river. If I were rowing upstream and downstream, would it take me just as long if there were no current or if there were a current? You might say, well, if you row upstream you're slowed down, but if you rowed downstream you sped up and it all comes out in the wash. But that's not true. And the reason it's not true is very simple. If I row the boat upstream, because the river is trying to push me backwards, I'm spending a lot more time on the slow leg of the trip. I'm spending a lot more time when I'm fighting against the river than when I come back and the river is speeding me up. And the result of spending more time going slowly, means the overall time takes longer. It actually also takes longer to go across the river and back, because I've got to angle myself a little ways upstream to land on the opposite shore. But that effect is much less because I'm not working directly against the current. You can work out the mathematics of this if you want using the Pythagorean theorem. But you don't need to. Take my word for it, it takes longer to go upstream and back than it does to go across the wind and back again.

So, if there is an ether wind blowing past the Earth, and we orient this apparatus so one leg is in the direction of the wind and the other leg is perpendicular to it, then we should be able to see a difference in travel times for the light beams.

How are we going to detect that difference? Well, that was the genius of the Michelson-Morley experiment. And, incidentally, this design is used to this very day as a sensitive measurement of distances or optical properties, because the clever idea that Michelson-Morley had works so well and is so very, very sensitive.

So let's take a look at how it works. To do that, we need to understand the phenomenon of *wave interference*. So the picture I'm showing here has a little picture of the Michelson-Morley apparatus in the upper right corner to remind you what we're talking about. Wave interference is the following thing: When two waves combine, as they do in the Michelson-Morley experiment after they've gone their separate paths and come back together again, they may be in step with each other, as I show for two waves here. These two waves are exactly in step. This is what would happen if they had traveled identical paths in identical times. They would be in step, and when they combined they would make a wave that was bigger. That's one possibility. That's called *constructive interference*. The waves combine constructively to make a bigger wave. We're going to see more about interference later, when we get to quantum physics. So, that's one possibility for interference.

On the other hand, what if the path lengths are different or the times that are taken are different because of the ether wind, and the two waves arrive slightly out of step? In fact, what if they're out of step by just the right amount that the crests, the peak of one wave, line up with the troughs of the other? Then when those waves combine, we get nothing. Darkness. No light. That's wave interference. What's happening in the Michelson-Morley experiment is we're combining two waves that have traveled on two different paths. If the path lengths are identical and the speeds of light are identical, they're going to come back in step. We're going to get constructive interference. If the path lengths are identical but the speeds are different, we're going to get different interference. It may be destructive. It may be partially destructive.

In fact, the situation is a little bit more complicated than that. The light beam is not perfectly straight, but it spreads out a little bit and parts of the light travel at slight angles. And they travel slightly different paths. And the result of all this is, what an observer looking in the viewer sees is something like this. This is an actual photograph taken by putting a camera at the viewer of a Michelson-Morley experiment. And what you see are a band of what are called *interference fringes*. You see light and dark and light and dark and light and dark. This particular one was done with a red laser light. The same kind of red lasers you see in supermarket checkouts. That's why we have that color.

So, we see alternating bands of light and dark. The light bands, the bright bands, are due to waves that traveled the two paths and came back interfering constructively. The dark regions are due to waves that came back and interfered destructively. And again, because light is leaving the source at slightly different angles and traveling just slightly different distances, we get this whole range of bands. Here is why it doesn't matter that we build the apparatus with exactly the same length arms; I don't care if the arm lengths are different. That will just make the interference pattern shift slightly right to left. But once I build the apparatus, that interference pattern will sit there and it will look like that unless something changes.

And here's the key to how the experiment works. Michelson-Morley said, let's do this experiment now, when the Earth is going this way—relative in its orbit around the sun. We'll get a certain interference pattern. Let's do the experiment again six months later when the Earth is moving in a different direction. And if the interference pattern shifts—and that's all that matters—if the interference pattern shifts, then we know that the change in the orientation of the apparatus relative to the ether wind caused a change in the relative times it took the light to travel the two different paths. We don't care absolutely how long it took to travel those paths, we don't care that the paths were the same length. All we want to know is, is there a shift in the interference fringes.

Not only do we do the experiment at different times of year, but we also do the experiment at different orientations. And that's why Michelson and Morley floated their apparatus in a great big bath of liquid mercury. OSHA would have a big problem with all that liquid mercury and mercury fumes today. But they floated the whole thing on a big stone slab—which floats in mercury because stone is less dense than liquid mercury—and they were able to rotate the entire apparatus.

Why did they need to do that? Well, several reasons. Suppose it happened that they started out in a situation where the apparatus happened to be aligned with one of its paths along the ether wind. So here's the apparatus, once again, I'm showing now a big picture of the whole apparatus with the light beams. And here comes the ether wind. So the ether wind, in this picture, is blowing from right to left. The whole apparatus is immersed in this ether wind that's blowing past the Earth. And in this configuration, we expect the travel time for light, on what in the picture is the horizontal path—remember, the whole apparatus, though, is lying horizontally on the Earth—we expect a longer travel time on this path than we do on this path.

Now, we're not going to know that just by looking at one interference pattern. We're just going to see one pattern of interference looking in the viewer—a sequence of light and dark bands. We don't know which path is longer at this point and which path is shorter, because we don't know if the two paths have exactly the same length, and so on. That's not important. What's important is what happens if we say, okay now let's rotate the apparatus to different angles. I mean, it might have been, we don't know which way the ether wind is blowing. We might not have had this configuration. Let's rotate the apparatus to a different orientation. There it is in a different orientation. If this picture is correct, and the ether wind is blowing at us from the right, then in this case the two paths are going to take the same amount of time if they have the same length. Whether they have the same length or not, that's not crucial.

What's crucial is the interference pattern we get, in this case, is going to be shifted somewhat from what it was before. Because the light path, the light traveling the two different paths is going to take different amounts of time than it did before. And consequently, we're going to see a shift in the interference pattern as we rotate the apparatus. Let's rotate it another 45 degrees until it's now 90 degrees from where it was before.

Now, this beam, which originally was going against and with the ether wind, is now going across it. So now the travel time on this path is shorter. And the travel time on this path, which was originally the path that was perpendicular to the wind, this path is now parallel to the wind and its travel time is longer. And that's going to result, again, in a shift of those interference fringes. And I want to emphasize this about this experiment; this is not an experiment to measure the speed of light in two mutually perpendicular directions. It's an experiment to determine whether the speed of light differs in two mutually different, mutually perpendicular, directions. And the way we detect that difference is by looking at the interference pattern. In one case, we learn nothing from that single case. We rotate the apparatus and we see if the interference pattern shifts. And the amount of shift tells us something about how different the times were along those two paths.

So you say, well, maybe Michelson and Morley just could have done this experiment in one day just sitting there rotating the apparatus and seeing how much the interference pattern shifts. But they had a worry about that. They were worried, what if, by some unlucky chance, on the day they chose to do the experiment, the Earth in its orbital motion happened, at that moment, to coincide with the ether. So at that moment the Earth happened to be at rest with respect to the ether.

Now, that doesn't bother us so much. That doesn't violate the Copernican paradigm so much, because it's okay instantaneously, by chance, for the Earth to happen to be at rest relative to ether. Pretty soon it's not going to be. And, in fact, six months later, it's going to be moving in the opposite direction in its 20-mile-a-second orbit around the sun. That'll give it a 40-mile-a-second speed difference from when it was at rest with the ether. And, so, if we do the experiment at different times of year, we should be able definitely to detect this change in the interference pattern and, therefore, the motion of the Earth through the ether.

Well, what happened when the experiment was done in 1887? What happened was, there was never, never, in any orientation, at any time of year, there was never any shift in the interference pattern. None. No shift. No fringe shift. Nothing. What's the implication? Here's an experiment that was done to measure the speed of the Earth and direction of the Earth's motion through the ether. It was an experiment that was 10 times more sensitive than it needed to be. It could have detected speeds as low as two miles a second, instead of the known 20 miles a second that the Earth has in its orbital motion around the sun. It didn't detect it.

What's the conclusion from the Michelson-Morley experiment? Well, the conservative conclusion is, there's no fringe shift. But what's the implication of that conclusion? The implication of that conclusion is the Earth is not moving relative to the ether. If the Earth were moving relative to the ether, the path lengths, the times to travel the two paths in the Michelson-Morley apparatus would have differed, either at different times of year or in different orientations. We would have detected that as a shift in the interference pattern. A shift that was easily measurable for speeds much less than the known speed of the Earth in its orbit. And we would have seen that shift. No shift. So-called null result. One of the most famous experiments in physics did not give the result it was intended to give.

Michelson and Morley confidently expected their experiment would measure the direction and speed of the Earth's motion through the ether. Result, zero. No interference pattern shift. No fringe shift. No motion through the ether.

Now, think back to the logic that got us to this point. We argued that the Earth is either at rest with respect to the ether or it's not at rest with respect to the ether. We ruled out it being at rest with respect to the ether, because we ruled out Earth alone among all the things in the universe being at rest—that totally violated the Copernican paradigm. We ruled out the possibility that there was a blob of ether surrounding the Earth that was being dragged along with Earth. So, locally, the Earth was taking the ether in its vicinity with us, and, locally, the Earth was at rest with respect to the ether. We ruled that out from the observations of aberration of starlight. That ruled out the possibility that Earth is not moving relative to the ether. The only possibility left is the possibility that Earth is moving with respect to ether. That has got to be true. We're forced to that conclusion by the beginning of this lecture.

Now, we've gone through the Michelson-Morley experiment. Null result. No fringe shift. No detection of any change in the speed of light in different directions. Conclusion, the speed of light is the same in all directions. How could that be? That could be only if the Earth is at rest with respect to the ether, because as I described earlier with that sound example, if the Earth is moving through the ether, then the speed light will differ in different directions. And that's exactly what the Michelson-Morley experiment was designed to detect.

So we have a real serious contradiction. We've ruled out the possibility that the Earth is at rest with respect to the ether. We confidently do an experiment that's designed to show us exactly how fast and in what direction Earth is moving relative to the ether. The experiment is sensitive enough to measure that. And it gets the answer, zero. It says the Earth is not moving with respect to the ether. And that's exactly the possibility we ruled out.

That's a deep and serious contradiction that hits physics in the 1800s, particularly in 1887. How can that be? Well, it took a lot of physicists thinking about that. What could be going wrong? Is there something wrong with the basic hypothesis of the Michelson-Morley experiment? Is the experiment not sensitive enough? No. The experiment is sensitive enough. Does wave interference not really occur? No. Wave interference had been discovered, for light, in the early 1800s and was a well-known phenomenon. Light was known to be a wave. It was known to interfere. There's nothing new in all that. What's new is that Michelson and Morley are masters of experimental technique and were able to put together an experiment that was clearly and demonstrably able to measure the effect they were looking for.

So, what could be wrong? Well, there were some hypotheses developed. The Irish physicist Fitzgerald and a Dutch physicist Lorentz, both pretty much independently came up with one hypothesis. And these two physicists deserve some of the credit for the development of relativity, because their hypothesis was, in one sense, correct and in another sense not correct. They assumed that somehow the motion of the experiment through the ether caused the whole apparatus to compress in the direction it was moving. As though the push against the ether—which is strange, because the ether doesn't exert any resistance to objects like planets moving through it—somehow the push against the ether or something, caused the apparatus to shrink. If the apparatus shrank, let's look at that apparatus again, in the direction of its motion, then this leg, the leg running parallel to the ether wind, the leg on which light was going to take a longer time to travel because it had to go upstream and then come back, if that length were shortened by just the right amount, that would compensate for the longer travel time, the slower speed of light going against the ether wind. And Fitzgerald and Lorentz proposed that that's what happened. They called this, it's now called the Lorentz-Fitzgerald contraction hypothesis, sometimes just called the Lorentz contraction, they calculated how much that contraction would have to be in terms of the speed of light and the speed of the apparatus relative to the ether, and they found there was an answer they could get that would allow that effect to go away; it would allow the experiment to give no fringe shift, the experiment to be unable to measure the speed of the Earth relative to ether because the whole apparatus had shrunk. It's a strange hypothesis. It's an ad hoc hypothesis. We'll see later that it has seeds of truth in it, but it has absolutely no theoretical basis. And it still assumes that there is an absolute frame of reference in which, if we put this apparatus, it has the right length, and if you move it relative to the ether it somehow gets squished. A very ad hoc assumption no physics behind it, no theoretical basis. Very unsatisfying.

This is now the late 1800s. The stage is set for 1905 when Albert Einstein is going to come on the scene, and Einstein and his resolution of this contradiction will be the topic of our next lecture.

Lecture Seven

Einstein to the Rescue

Scope:

In 1905, Einstein resolved the contradiction. He discarded the ether concept and with it, any meaning that could be attached to statements such as "I am at rest" and "I am moving." Instead, he asserted that the principle of relativity holds for *all* of physics, including not only mechanics but electromagnetism as well. Simple though this statement of *the special theory of relativity* is, its implications are profound—requiring a radical restructuring of our notions of space and time.

Outline

I. In 1905, after ten years of pondering the nature of light and of time, Einstein resolved the contradiction with his *special theory of relativity*.

  A. Personal and historical notes.

    1. As early as age 16, Einstein had puzzled about what a light beam would look like if one ran alongside it at speed *c*—a puzzle that he eventually solved with relativity.

    2. Einstein was twenty-six and a young father at the time of his 1905 paper on special relativity. He was working in the Swiss patent office because he had not been able to secure an academic position. In that same year, he published three other scientific papers, two of which were also seminal works. One provided the final convincing evidence for the existence of atoms, and the other helped lay the groundwork for quantum physics.

    3. Even though I have stressed the logical dilemma posed by the Michelson-Morley result, historians of science debate whether Einstein even considered this result in developing his theory of relativity. Einstein's reasoning was based at least as much on how he felt nature should be as it was on experimental results.

  B. Einstein declared the ether to be a fiction in his paper "On the Electrodynamics of Moving Bodies." Instead, he asserted the principle of relativity for all of physics, electromagnetism as well as mechanics. Thus, the essence of

Einstein's theory is summed up in a single statement, the *principle of special relativity*:

The laws of physics are the same for all observers in uniform motion.

1. What's *special* about special relativity is the restriction to the case of uniform motion (later, we will take up the general theory, which removes this restriction).
2. Historical note: Einstein actually proposed two postulates as the basis of his theory: the principle of relativity and the constancy of the speed of light. A more modern approach is to consider the latter a consequence of
   the former.

C. Einstein's relativity is both radical and conservative—conservative because it asserts for electromagnetism what had long been true in mechanics, namely that motion doesn't matter (recall Galilean relativity from Lecture Three). Relativity is radical because it radically alters our notions of time and space.

D. From a modern perspective, Einstein's relativity should come as no surprise. You already agreed to the principle of relativity in Lecture One, when you recognized that both tennis (mechanics) and microwave ovens (electromagnetism) should work the same in any uniformly moving reference frame.

E. Special relativity is really more than a theory; it has been verified and is unlikely to be refuted.

II. Why did it take a genius like Einstein to recognize the truth of relativity? Because relativity requires us to relinquish deeply ingrained ideas about space and time.

A. The principle of relativity means that the laws of physics are exactly the same for all observers in uniform motion.

B. In particular, the predictions of Maxwell's electromagnetic equations will be the same for all observers.

    1. One such prediction is the existence of electromagnetic waves—including light—that travel with speed *c*. Therefore, all observers will measure the same value *c* for the speed of light—*even though different observers are moving with respect to (or relative to) each other*!

    2. To see what this means, imagine I'm standing by the roadside, equipped with a device for measuring the speed of light. The device uses a very fast clock to time the passage of light over a known distance of exactly 1meter. You drive by in a car at 70 mph that is equipped with an identical apparatus. Down the road, a traffic signal flashes, and we both measure the speed of the light as it passes us. Despite the fact that we're in relative motion, we both get exactly the same speed for the light! We get the same results if we repeat the experiment with you going past in a jet plane at 600 mph or even in a spacecraft at half the speed of light!

    3. How can this be? It's possible only if our measures of time and space are different. Time and space are not absolute, but are relative to a particular observer.

Essential Reading:

Mook and Vargish, *Inside Relativity*, Chapter 3, Sections 1–6.

Hoffmann, *Relativity and Its Roots*, Chapter 5, pp. 81–95.

Suggested Reading:

Einstein and Infeld, *The Evolution of Physics*, Chapter 3, pp. 187–209.

Questions to Consider:

1. The speed of light is the same for anyone who cares to measure it. Explain how this fact follows from the principle of relativity.

2. The observer standing by the roadside in our example measures *c* for the speed of the light from the traffic signal. If you didn't know about relativity, what speeds would you infer for the light as measured by observers in the car, the airplane, and the spaceship?

3. What's wrong with the following explanation of the fact that all observers in our example get the same value for the speed of light? "Strange things happen to time and space when you move, so the moving observers' clocks and meter sticks are distorted in just such a way that they all get the same value for the speed of light as does the stationary observer."

Measuring the Speed of Light

Here, the observer is standing still and records a speed of 186,000 m/s (c) for a burst of light from the traffic signal.

Now, the observer is riding in a car, driven at 70 mph toward the traffic signal. When she measures the speed of light, it still comes out to 186,000 m/s.

Here, the observer is riding in an airplane, flying at 600 mph toward the traffic signal. When she measures the speed of light here, it *still* comes out to 186,000 m/s.

Finally, the observer is riding in a spaceship, traveling at one half the speed of light toward the traffic signal. When she measures the speed of light here, it *still* comes out to 186,000 m/s. The speed of light is the same in all frames of reference.

Light Source

Burst of light

c

70 mph

600 mph

$\frac{1}{2}$ speed c

Lecture Seven—Transcript
Einstein to the Rescue

It's now the year 1905, and physicists have been puzzling for several decades over the null result of the Michelson-Morley experiment. Why was there no fringe shift? Why didn't we detect the Earth's motion relative to the ether? The best we have going is the Lorenz-Fitzgerald contraction hypothesis suggesting the apparatus got compressed. The idea being that all objects perhaps get compressed in the direction of their motion relative to the ether. Physicists are reluctant to give up this notion of the ether for reasons that will be very obvious in just a moment. You may think we can give it up but hold on.

Let me begin with a few historical touches here about Einstein and the year 1905 and what Einstein was like. One hears a lot about Einstein. One hears, for example, that he was actually rather dull as a child. That's not true. But what he was in school was very rebellious. And some of the trouble he got into in several schools, especially a very rigorous German school he attended, was that he simply couldn't put up with rigorous discipline. He wanted to study and work on his own, and this led him to problems throughout his academic career. But he was not dull. He was noted for his intelligence, although he didn't necessarily do well in all his courses. In particular, he didn't do particularly well in some mathematics courses. And one of his mathematics professors, named Herman Minkowski, was very distressed about this. And Minkowski, nevertheless, later went on to become a major interpreter of relativity and mathematical terms. So Einstein was a rebel, but he wasn't dull.

There's also a rumor that he talked rather late. And this is probably true. And Einstein, himself, probably embellished this a little bit. He claimed at some point that he didn't talk until he was three years old. And, perhaps, his talking late had something to do with a brain in which he could visualize abstract ideas better than most of us can. I don't know about that.

Einstein was an interesting character. Although he published his paper on the special theory of relativity in 1905 and wrote it in a matter of only about six weeks after he got the key insight that led to the idea, he had been thinking about this problem for many, many years—when he was 16, for about 10 years, in fact. When he was 16, he asked the question, "What would a light wave look like if I ran along side it at the speed of light?" That's an interesting question. It may have occurred to some of you also. Why is it an interesting question? Well, it's a particularly interesting question because if you believe Maxwell's theory of electromagnetism, you know that that theory predicts the existence of light waves, and light waves should move at speed c. If you run along a light wave at speed c, you see a structure that looks like a light wave—electric and magnetic fields, in the particular configuration of a light wave—but it's not moving relative to you. That's not a solution of Maxwell's equations.

If you believe in the ether paradigm, you simply say, "Well, I'm not in the ether frame of reference so I don't expect Maxwell's equations to be correct. I don't expect the laws of electromagnetism to work in this frame of reference." But Einstein puzzled about this. He really worried, what would a light beam look like if I ran along side it?

Another thing that bothered Einstein came out of shaving. He's sitting there looking in the mirror, and he wondered, "What if I started to run with this mirror in front of me? Walk along. Still continue to shave. No problem. What if I run faster? What if I run at the speed of light? The light leaving my face that's going to bounce off the mirror is never going to get to the mirror, because the mirror's moving away at the speed of light. So as I reach the speed of light, will the mirror suddenly go dark?" By the way, *Einstein's Mirror* is the title of one of the more recent books I've put in my bibliography for this course. You might be interested in reading it. It draws its name from this particular pondering of Einstein's.

"What would happen if I ran at the speed of light? The light wouldn't be able to catch the mirror. The mirror would go dark." Well, those are things Einstein pondered about, before 1905. When he reached 1905, he was still a young man. He was only 26 years old. Most of us think of Einstein as in the picture I'm showing here, as a very old, rather interesting looking character with this grizzled face and this wild, white hair. We forget that Einstein did some of his most creative work, in fact, basically all his most creative work, as a very young man. And in 1905, the year he formulated the special theory of relativity, Einstein was a young father. Twenty-six years old. That's four years beyond college graduation age. He had a young child and a young wife who was a fellow physics student of his. And he was working in a position as a patent clerk in the Swiss patent office. He actually enjoyed that position because he was working with patents and technological devices. So, that was interesting to him. He also had plenty of spare time to work on his own ideas in physics, including the theory of relativity.

Why was he a patent clerk rather than a physics professor? Because of all the classmates of his from his graduate school class, he was the only one who was not recommended for a professorship upon graduation. He had trouble finding an academic position. Again, not because he wasn't smart, but because he walked to his own drummer. He was a rebel. He was difficult to work with in an institutional setting. He simply was not recommended for a professorship. And it was a while before he achieved a professorship. Once his relativity fame became established, it was no problem for him.

But in 1905, he is working in the Swiss patent office. He's watching a lot of trains and clock towers in Switzerland. Thinking a lot about time and space. And he's writing papers. And he actually published a number of papers in 1905—four significant papers and some smaller ones. And of the four substantial papers, three of them were really seminal in the history of physics. One of them, the one I'm going to talk about today, is the paper that introduced to the world special relativity.

The second paper was a paper that was on the subject of Brownian motion, which is the behavior of very small particles—little dust motes, or little bacteria, or things like that—that you might see through a microscope as they're jostled around by the invisible particles that make up, say, a solution like water. And Einstein published a paper on Brownian motion. And that was the paper that convinced the few remaining skeptics—in 1905 there were still some skeptics who didn't believe there were atoms, they didn't believe in the reality of atoms—and Einstein's paper on Brownian motion convinced the remaining skeptics of the reality of atoms. So, that was a seminal paper in physics.

The third important paper is one I'll have a lot more to say about later in the course when we deal with quantum physics, because Einstein interpreted the results of the so-called *photoelectric effect* experiment—which, again, we'll describe in detail—to give an interpretation in terms of the new quantum ideas. He was the second person to introduce the idea of the quantum. He was the first person to apply it to the nature of light. And I'll have a lot more to say about that. That was a really crucial and important paper.

And the fourth paper of the batch of four significant papers was not particularly interesting. It was a run of the mill paper. Later in that year, he also published a paper in which he introduced the seeds of the idea behind the equation $E=mc^2$. And I'll have a lot more to say about that. But at this point, suffice it to say that $E=mc^2$, which you may think of as the essence of relativity, was not even in the original paper on relativity that was published in 1905.

So, what did Einstein have to say? He published a paper, which was not called the special theory of relativity, it was called, "On the Electrodynamics of Moving Bodies." And I want to emphasize that title, because I argued, when I introduced you to electromagnetism, that electromagnetism was crucial in understanding the evolution of relativity theory. Relativity is, really, an outgrowth of electromagnetism. And you now know why. It's because electromagnetism raised the questions, with respect to what does light go at speed c, in what frame of reference are the laws of electromagnetism valid? A question that had already been answered for mechanics, for the study of motion, way back in Galileo's time, and that now begged for an answer in terms of electromagnetism. And we've been looking for that answer. And we got some logic that told us that the answer should be: There is some motion relative to the ether. And then we did the Michelson-Morley experiment and found there was no answer to that question. We are still left with that question—in what frame of reference are the laws of electromagnetism valid? And Einstein's paper, a direct outgrowth of electromagnetism, was called, "On the Electrodynamics of Moving Bodies."

By the way, I have to give you one other historical aside here, which I find fascinating and a real reflection of Einstein's genius. There is, among historians of science today, still some debate about how much the Michelson-Morley result influenced Einstein's thinking. There have been some people who've argued in the past that he may not even have known about the Michelson-Morley result. That's probably not the case. He makes reference in his paper to "unsuccessful attempts to find the light medium." He's surely referring there to some of the early experiments at trying to detect Earth's motion through the ether. And he may well be referring to the Michelson-Morley experiment. But how much the Michelson-Morley experiment influenced his thought, we don't know. And it may not have been very much. For us, learning about relativity, it's crucial to understand the Michelson-Morley experiment because we need that absolute hard and fast logic that tells us inexorably we have to get to relativity.

Einstein, who thought about how the world ought to be, and said, "I think the world ought to be simple, I think it ought to behave this way," he may not even have thought much about the Michelson-Morley experiment. He may have thought, instead, that this is just the way the world has to be. I need a simpler world than the one I see. And here's the theory that describes that.

So what did Einstein do? Well, basically, he declared the ether to be a fiction. Something you may have had at the back of your mind in the last few lectures. Why are we going to all this trouble about the ether if we're going to have trouble finding the Earth's motion through it? The problem is, once you give up the idea of ether, you're left with that question, with respect to what does light go at speed c? In what frame of reference are the laws of electromagnetism valid?

So what did Einstein do? He declared the ether as a fiction. No more ether. And he asserted, instead, the principle of relativity; the same principle of relativity that Galileo had talked about. The principle of relativity that in Galileo's time said the laws of physics are the same for all observers in uniform motion. And it said that because in Galileo's time the laws of motion were basically all there was to physics pretty much. We've modified that since to say, Galilean relativity states the laws of motion, the laws of mechanics, are valid in all uniformly moving frames of reference. And then we introduce this new branch of physics—electromagnetism. And we ask the same question for electromagnetism, in what frame of reference are the laws of electromagnetism valid, with respect to what frame of reference does light go at speed c?

Well, Einstein declared the ether was a fiction. And he asserted the principle of relativity again, for all of physics. In that sense, relativity is a profoundly conservative step. What had been known for hundreds of years—that the laws of physics or the laws of mechanics, at least, didn't depend on your state of motion as long as that motion was uniform—that had been known for hundreds of years. That's the Galilean principle of relativity. Einstein simply reasserted that relativity was true for all of physics. It's that simple.

And I introduced you to this idea in the very first lecture. And I introduced you to it through the microwave oven and the tennis match. The tennis match represents motion—mechanics. The microwave oven represents electromagnetism. And I think you drew the conclusion in your mind that it made eminent sense, that both those things, the game of tennis, a physics experiment in mechanics, and the microwave oven, a physics experiment in electromagnetism, would work the same on the cruise ship, on Venus, and even on that distant planet in a distant galaxy moving away from Earth at 80 percent of the speed of light.

So to you, this probably makes very good sense. In fact, it probably makes more sense to us at the turn of the 21st century than it did to people at the turn of the twentieth century who were steeped in the idea that there had to be an ether. To us we know about the existence of distant galaxies moving away at 80 percent of the speed of light. And it makes eminent sense that microwave ovens should work the same there as they do here. So, I think you can accept what Einstein had to say, at least at present, in a sort of gut way that maybe wouldn't have been possible around 100 years ago. You can accept the principle that laws of physics are simply the same, all laws of physics, for anybody who is in uniform motion, in any reference frame, uniform motion. And that is all Einstein said. That is it.

Let's take a look at that statement. It's an important statement. It's special relativity. The statement of special relativity is, simply, the statement that the laws of physics are the same for all observers in uniform motion. And that's it.

I want to make a couple of comments about this statement. I mean, you can assert that to your friends and say, I know everything there is to know about Einstein's special theory of relativity. Because that is everything there is to say about it. The laws of physics, all the laws of physics, are the same for everybody in uniform motion. Any frame of reference in uniform motion is an equally good place for doing physics. Period. And that's it.

A couple of comments though. First of all, if you read Einstein's original paper, and you read older textbooks that talk about this, you'll find that Einstein didn't quite put it this simply. He had what he called two postulates. One postulate was this one—that the laws of physics are the same for all observers. And the other postulate, which he said seemed to be in contradiction with this but wasn't, is that the speed of light is independent of the speed of its source. I gave you some observational evidence earlier why that was the case. Why we know that's the case that the speed of light doesn't depend on the speed of the source, that evidence involving double star systems. Einstein asserted that as a second postulate. I think a more modern way of looking at relativity is to simply state this principle: That the laws of physics are the same for all observers in uniform motion. All frames of reference in uniform motion are equally good places for doing physics—that includes experiments in electromagnetism and measurements of the speed of light. And we'll get to that in just a minute.

So this suffices. One statement. The laws of physics are the same for everybody as long as they're in uniform motion. There is no preferred frame of reference. There is no preferred state of motion. The Earth is not special. That distant planet in that galaxy moving with respect to Earth at 80 percent of the speed of light, that is not special. No place, no state of motion is special, at least as long as it's uniform motion.

That gets to the second point I want to make about the statement of special relativity. You hear the word "special" you might think this is kind of neat. And you know, really super. Special doesn't mean that in this context. Special means this is a specialized theory. It applies only to a limited, special case. It applies to the case of uniform motion only. In the context of special relativity, nonuniform motion doesn't count. The laws of physics are not the same, at least in the paradigm of special relativity, in frames of reference that are undergoing non-uniform motion, that are accelerating, that are changing speed, that are rotating, that are airplanes going through turbulence, that are cruise ships in rough seas, that are planets in circular motion around their stars, maybe, that one's a subtle one, and we'll get to that later. In fact, as I argued a little earlier, it's sometimes difficult to decide whether we have a frame of reference in uniform motion. And all of special relativity has a slightly slippery foundation for that reason.

There is a general theory of relativity that generalizes this statement to all motion. That takes away the in uniform motion clause. But it's a much more difficult theory. We'll spend less time on it. But we will get to it later on in the course.

So, for now, we are talking about special relativity. And special relativity means specialized to the case of uniform motion. It doesn't say everybody is equal as far as the laws of physics are concerned. It does say everybody who is in uniform motion is equal as far as the laws of physics are concerned.

If you can find one frame of reference that's in uniform motion and the Earth, although it's not quite, is moving uniformly enough that special relativity applies to the Earth to a very good approximation. Not perfectly. But to a very good approximation. If you can find one frame of reference that is essentially in uniform motion, then any other frame of reference that is moving at a constant speed in a fixed direction relative to that one must also be in uniform motion. So, if you can find one, you can find others. And we at least can find approximate uniformly moving frames of reference, such as the Earth and the other planets, and spaceships moving at constant speed in space and relative to, say, the Earth, and airplanes moving through calm air, and so on. So we have frames of reference in which this is true. But again, we're going to get further a little bit later.

It's going to be important though to remember that special relativity works only in uniformly moving frames of reference. Because we are going to come across a situation in the next few lectures where we do have some nonuniform motion. And you have to remember that, because that nonuniform motion, the laws of physics do not work when the motion is nonuniform.

Now, I asserted that Einstein's relativity is a very conservative statement. It's a conservative statement because it reasserted, for all of physics, particularly for electromagnetism, what had already been true for the physics of motion—for Newton's laws, for the classical physics that came before the study of electromagnetism. Einstein reasserted relativity. He's very conservative. He says what Galileo already knew is now true for all of physics. But it's not only conservative, it's also radical. And it's radical because, as you will see in the rest of this lecture, it does very, very strange things to our notions of space and time. And that's what most people think of when they think of relativity. They think of $E=mc^2$. But then they immediately think of things like the twin example that I started this course with—an example that we will revisit in a couple lectures in some detail and understand exactly why it has to be.

Relativity does strange things to space and time. I didn't want to emphasize that up until now, because I want you to understand that relativity is much simpler than that. Relativity is the statement that the laws of physics are the same for all observers in uniform motion. And I want you to have two feelings about that statement. One is it makes good gut sense. Why is Earth special? Why should Earth or any other frame of reference be special? In an era when we know about distant galaxies moving away from Earth at 80 percent of the speed of light, it makes no sense to think that the laws of physics work here on Earth or in some frame of reference that Earth's not moving very fast relative to, but then they certainly don't work in that distant galaxy. What's so special about us? Nothing. So, it makes good gut sense.

I also want you to understand the inexorable logic that led us to it. The question: In what frame of reference are the laws of electromagnetism valid? The attempts to answer that question in nineteenth century physic's terms with the ether, the contradiction that said the Earth is not at rest with respect to the ether. Then the Michelson-Morley experiment coming along and said but the Earth is at rest with respect to the ether. That contradiction. We were driven inexorably to that.

The reason I want you to think both about your gut feel and that logic is because in the next few lectures we are going to be doing those very strange things to space and time. And you will find those things unacceptable. You will want to fight against them intellectually. But they must be the case. And they must be the case if you believe this simple statement that the laws of physics, all laws of physics, including electromagnetism, are the same for all observers in uniform motion. If you believe that, and you have the logic leading you to it, and you have the gut feel for a universe which is so vast and full of objects moving at such high speeds, that it ought to make sense. So this is the simple statement of relativity. This is special relativity. The laws of physics are the same for all observers in uniform motion.

By the way, although this is often called the theory of relativity, I really like to avoid the word theory, because it conjures up in most people's minds the idea this is just a theory. You know, evolution is just a theory. We shouldn't be teaching it in schools, because it's just a theory. We don't know if it's true. Well, that's hogwash. It's hogwash about evolution, and it's hogwash about relativity. Relativity, special relativity particularly, is one of the most solidly verified "theories" in all of physics. It's much more correctly verified than Newton's laws, which turn out only to be an approximation. Special relativity is true to many, many decimal places of accurate measurement as far as we can tell. It is a very accurate description of physical reality, at least when we are dealing with frames of reference in uniform motion. And we're avoiding questions of gravity. We'll get to those and general relativity.

So, I don't like to think of special relativity as a theory. Sure, it's a theory. Could it be proved wrong? Very, very, very unlikely. Could it be modified slightly? Probably not. It may be expanded upon, with the general theory of relativity, and maybe something beyond that, but it's not wrong. It's not *just* a theory. It is really one of the foundations of our understanding of physical reality. And along with it go these very strange things that happen to space and time.

Now, let me get to those things now. Why, after all, did it take Einstein's genius to come up with special relativity? Here it is, a simple statement. You can go out and make this statement to your friends. I know relativity. The laws of physics are the same for all observers in uniform motion. And that is really it. There is nothing else to it than that statement. There is no other foundation. From that, all else follows. And if you ever get stuck in relativity, just go back to that statement. It's all there. Why was that so hard? Well, Einstein puzzled about it for 10 years. And six weeks, roughly, before the paper on special relativity was finalized, Einstein said, "I suddenly got the answer." The key was time. Einstein was able to give up his commonsense notion of time and accept something very strange and different about the way time behaves. And then he was easily able to come up with the special theory of relativity. And everything went ahead from there.

To see why it took an Einstein to do that, though, let's take a little bit more logic from this statement. Okay, here's the special theory of relativity or the special relativity—the laws of physics are the same for all observers in uniform motion. Einstein's statement in 1905. This includes electromagnetism. For the first time, Einstein brought electromagnetism under the same relativity principle that had already governed mechanics. And part of electromagnetism—and this is why I spent a whole lecture on electromagnetism and showed you Maxwell's equations and all the mathematics of them, because I wanted you to see that they led inexorably to the prediction of electromagnetic waves and that those electromagnetic waves move at a known, calculable speed c, 186,000 miles a second, etc.—includes that prediction.

In what frame of reference are the laws of electromagnetism valid? That's the question we've been asking for two lectures. Now we have Einstein's answer. And it's a very simple answer. For any observer in uniform motion, in any frame of reference in uniform motion, the laws of electromagnetism are valid. Any frame of reference in uniform motion. What that means is all predictions of electromagnetic theory are valid in any frame of reference in uniform motion, including the prediction that electromagnetic waves travel at speed c. And what that means is the answer to our second question: With respect to what does light go at speed c? Which we saw was equivalent to the question: In what frame of reference are the laws of electromagnetism valid? The answer to that question must also be the speed of light is c with respect to any uniformly moving frame of reference. Any uniformly moving observer will measure c for the speed of light. So, therefore, all observers in uniform motion will measure the same value for the speed of light.

So far so good. That is a direct consequence of our belief in the fact that the laws of physics are the same in all frames of reference in uniform motion. All laws of physics, including, as Einstein added, the laws of electromagnetism, with their prediction that there are light waves and those light waves move at the speed we call c. That prediction must be true in all uniformly moving frames of reference. Therefore, anybody who's in uniform motion measures the speed of some light, and they get the answer c for that speed. And here's where it gets difficult for you—even if they are moving relative to each other. And I believe that was difficult for Einstein. I believe it's difficult for any of us, in our gut, to accept this. But it has to be true if you accept the principle of relativity. If you accept the principle of relativity, then it must be true that all observers, as long as they're moving uniformly, will measure the same value for the speed of light. Even if they're moving relative to each other.

I want to give you an example that illustrates that. Let me begin with a picture of the example. We're going to try to measure the speed of light. So here you are or here I am standing by the roadside. And I'm looking at a traffic light. And that traffic light is going to flash and emit some light waves. And those light waves are going to go by me at speed c. And I'm going to measure that speed by taking some simple measuring apparatus. I'm going to take a meter stick, a stick that is exactly one meter long. And I bought it from a reputable company so I know it's exactly one meter long. And I'm going to take a beautiful, perfect clock, which can measure very, very precise time intervals. And what I'm going to do is I'm going to notice with my clock when the light reaches the front end of my meter stick and when it passes the back end of my meter stick. I'm going to measure on my clock the time that takes. I'm going to take speed equals distance divided by time. And from that I'm going to calculate a speed for light.

Now, that's not actually how we calculate the speed of light, of course. This clock would never do. This distance, well, it's a little short, but actually we could measure the speed of light over this distance. My undergraduates at Middlebury College, by the way, in their sophomore year regularly measure the speed of light over a distance of about 30 feet. They send a laser beam down to a mirror about 30 feet away. It bounces back. And they use a high-speed clock—it's a device called an oscilloscope—that notices when the light beam leaves the laser and notices when the light beam returns and makes a little blip on a screen. And the distance between those blips is a measure of how long the distance is, the time is, between the departure and the return of the light beam. And they can measure the speed of light to an accuracy of about a tenth of a percent. In a simple undergraduate laboratory. Thanks to modern technology, particularly a laser that we can switch on and off in about a nanosecond, in about a billionth of a second that, by the way, was built by another undergraduate of mine.

So this is not a difficult thing to do. And with a little more fancy technology, but certainly within the realm of what we have, one could easily measure the speed of light over distances as short as a meter. One simply couldn't do it with this clock. But I'm going to pretend we can, or I'm going to pretend that this clock has the capabilities to measure the speed of light, to measure times as short as the time it takes light to go a meter very, very accurately. By the way, since the speed of light is 300,000 kilometers a second, that's 300 million meters a second, that time is one 300-millionth of a second. That's roughly the time a fast computer does a calculation. So it's not an unheard of kind of time. It's about three or four nanoseconds, because light travels one foot per nanosecond, and that's about three feet. A meter is about three feet. So it's not an immeasurable time. We regularly measure times a million times shorter than that in physics laboratories. So that's a reasonable measurement to try to make.

Now, here's what I'm going to do. So, I'm equipped with this meter stick and this clock. And I'm going to measure the speed of that light as it goes by me. Now, you're going to go past in a car at 70 miles an hour. Before you got in the car, I equipped you with an identical meter stick and an identical clock. And again, we bought them from the same reputable company. They came of the same manufacturing run. They are identical. Absolutely identical. You're going by in that car. You take your meter stick. You hold it up. You notice when the light passes the front of your meter stick. You notice when the light passes the back of your meter stick. You do the calculation of velocity equals distance divided by time. And you come up with an answer for the speed of light. You are moving relative to me at 70 miles an hour. If that picture I showed you of waves, speed, and the ether worked, you would measure a speed for c of 186,000 miles a second plus 70 miles an hour. Whatever that comes out to be. You don't. According to the principle of relativity, you measure exactly the same speed I do. Exactly. Well, I'll give you the number. It's 299,798,458 meters per second. That's the exact value for the speed of light. It's an exactly defined value. It's so well known that it's now used to set the standard measure of length. The meter is now defined in terms of the speed of light rather than the other way around.

And we get exactly the same value. Exactly. Even though you are moving relative to me at 70 miles an hour. How can that be? Worse, I'll put you instead in a jet plane. Again equipping you with the same clock and the same meter stick. Now you're going 600 miles an hour relative to me. You're in uniform motion. The laws of physics are equally valid for both of us. And you measure the same speed for the light. Exactly 299,792,458 meters per second. Same answer. Same light, also.

Let's make it even worse. I'm going to put you in a high-speed spaceship. And it's going to be going past me at half the speed of light. Are you going to get one-and-a-half c for the speed of light you measure? If you think you do, then you are thinking nonrelativistic. They say, "Oh, it's only on Earth that the speed is really c." There's something special about Earth. It's the special frame of reference. Nonsense. There is no special frame of reference. All frames of reference in uniform motion are equally valid. And both those observers will measure c for the speed of light.

And to make that clearer, let me take away the ground, which doesn't matter at all, and take away the traffic light—just some light going by and we're both going to measure it. And I'm—this is now from my point of view—I say, "Oh, I'm at rest, light's going by me at c, you're going by me at one-half c, and yet you measure the same speed for light that I do." You are equally equipped to say, or equally justified in saying, "Oh, I'm at rest in my spaceship and that other observer is going past me in the other direction at half c, because no frame of reference is preferred. All frames of reference in uniform motion are equally valid."

How can this possibly be? It must be that something funny has happened to clocks and meter sticks. But you're not justified in saying, "Oh, something funny happened to the spaceship measuring instruments, because the spaceship is moving." No, there is nothing special about your frame or the spaceship's frame. Something funny must have happened, not so much to the clocks and meter sticks, but to space and time themselves. And that is what we will be exploring in the next few lectures.

Lecture Eight
Uncommon Sense: Stretching Time

Scope:

The simple statement of relativity—that the laws of physics are the same for all observers in uniform motion—leads directly to absurd-seeming situations that violate our common-sense notions of space and time. But common sense is built of our limited experience, in which we never move at speeds anywhere near c relative to things in our immediate environment. Our common sense isn't wrong; it's just an approximation that works when relative speeds are small compared with c. But to describe the universe accurately and to understand what happens at high relative speeds, we need to abandon common sense and instead embrace the principle of relativity. When we do, we find that measures of time and space differ in different frames of reference.

Outline

I. Uncommon sense.

   A. The principle of relativity has brought us directly to an absurd-seeming situation: Different observers in relative motion measure the *same speed* for the same light. How can this be?

   B. This result seems absurd only because we believe time and space are the same for everyone—a notion deeply rooted in our everyday, common-sense experience.

      1. Common sense is built on limited experience. We simply don't move at speeds anywhere near c relative to the objects with which we interact. (We do move at speeds near c relative to distant galaxies and cosmic rays, but most of us aren't directly aware of that.)

      2. To appreciate the universe in all its richness, we need to abandon common sense and embrace the principle of relativity—with its disturbing implications for space and time.

      3. Our common-sense notions are not entirely wrong; they're just limited. The predictions of relativity agree almost perfectly with common sense when relative speeds are small compared with c.

   C. Watch your language!

1. It is all too easy to speak in a way that violates the principle of relativity; even many books on the subject do. We need to make an effort to be *relativistically correct* (RC) in describing what happens to space and time.
2. In the traffic light example, for instance, I can't dismiss your strange clock readings because "you're moving." That's because the principle of relativity denies the concept of absolute motion.
3. Both of us are equally positioned for doing physics, and your measurements in the spaceship zooming past Earth at $0.5c$ are every bit as good as mine on Earth.
4. It could be that the different clocks keep different time.

II. Let's consider the concept of "time dilation" or the stretching of time.

A. A "light clock" consists of a box containing a light source at one end and a mirror at the other. A flash of light leaves the source, bounces off the mirror, and returns to the source. This process repeats, so the round-trip travel time for the light constitutes the basic "ticking" of this clock. We want to examine the length of this "ticking"—that is, the time between the event of light leaving the source and returning to the source—in two different frames of reference.

1. First let's define "event": An event is something that happens at a time and a place.
2. To an observer at rest with respect to the light clock, the light makes a round-trip journey twice the long dimension of the box.
3. To an observer relative to whom the box is moving, the light takes a longer path, following two diagonals that are each longer than the long dimension of the box.
4. Here's where relativity comes in: The speed of the light is the *same* for both observers. Because the path lengths for the light are different, however, so must be the times between the emission of the light and its return to the source!

B. The phenomenon of different times for different observers of the light clock is called *time dilation*.

1. There's nothing special about the light clock; it's just a convenient device for visualizing why time dilation occurs. Times on ordinary clocks would show the same discrepancy.

2. Time dilation is not about light or light clocks; it's about *time itself*. Measures of time are simply different for different observers in motion relative to each other—a consequence of the principle of relativity.

3. Time dilation is often described by saying that "moving clocks run slow," but this is very poor wording and not RC (relativistically correct). Why not? Pause a minute and think about that question before proceeding. In particular, an observer moving with the light clock would feel *nothing unusual whatsoever*! Things wouldn't seem to be happening in slow motion nor would anything else seem strange. The frame of reference of the light clock is just as good as any other uniformly moving frame, so all physical events happen perfectly normally.

4. What time dilation really says is this: Suppose there are two events that occur at different places in some frame of reference; in that reference frame, the time between the events is measured by a pair of clocks at the two different places. If another clock moves so that it is present at both events, then the time between the events as measured on that single clock will be less than that measured by the pair of clocks.

5. Getting quantitative: Let t' be the time measured by the observer at rest with respect to the light clock, and t, the time measured by the observer for whom the box is moving. Then the two times are related by $t' = t\sqrt{1 - v^2}$ where v is the speed of the light clock relative to the observer for whom it's moving, with v given as a fraction of the speed of light (i.e., $v=0.5$ is half the speed of light). Anyone who remembers the Pythagorean theorem and who is fluent in high school algebra can derive this result, but we'll leave that as an exercise for those who want to try it.

Essential Reading:

Mook and Vargish, *Inside Relativity*, Chapter 3, Sections 7–10.

Hoffmann, *Relativity and Its Roots*, Chapter 5, pp. 96–106.

Hey and Walters, *Einstein's Mirror*, Chapter 3, pp. 46–55 (but watch out for relativistically incorrect wording in one heading!).

Suggested Reading:

Thorne, *Black Holes and Time Warps: Einstein's Outrageous Legacy*, Chapter 1.

Questions to Consider:

1. What's wrong with the statement "moving clocks run slow"? Can you find this or a similar "relativistically incorrect" statement in a book on relativity?

2. (For the mathematically courageous; you need not be able to do this to understand relativity!) Using high-school algebra and the Pythagorean theorem, derive the time-dilation equation $t' = t\sqrt{1 - v^2}$.

Time Dilation : A "Light Clock"

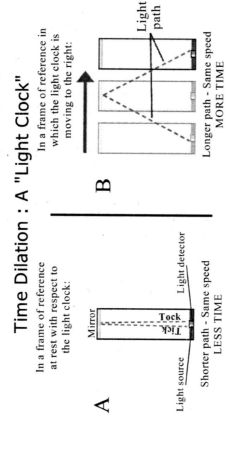

A

In a frame of reference at rest with respect to the light clock:

Mirror

Tick
Tock

Light source — Light detector

Shorter path - Same speed
LESS TIME

B

In a frame of reference in which the light clock is moving to the right:

Light path

Longer path - Same speed
MORE TIME

The light clock is a device that clearly shows how time dilation occurs. In this device, light is produced from a light source at the bottom of the clock, travels up the length of the light clock, bounces off a mirror, and returns to hit a light detector on the bottom of the clock. In A, a frame of reference in which the light clock is at rest with respect to the viewer, the path of the light is exactly equal to twice the height of the clock. In B, a frame of reference in which the light clock is moving to the right with respect to the viewer, the light path is longer. *But the speed of light has the same value for both observers and thus the time as measured in frame B is longer than the time recorded by clock A.*

TIME DILATION

~~"Moving clocks run slow"~~   *Bad Wording : Not RC !*

The time between two events is shorter when measured by a single clock present at both events than when measured by two different clocks located at the two events.

In this diagram, time dilation is explained in terms of "real" clocks rather than light clocks. Box One sets the stage for the experiment. Two clocks (B_1 and B_2) are located at two different places. Clock A is a clock whose state of motion is such that it will be present at B_1 and then later will be present at B_2. The two **events** that we are interested in are the concurrence of A with B_1 and the concurrence of A with B_2. Time dilation states that the time elapsed as recorded by clock A which is present at both events will be less than the elapsed time as recorded by the two other clocks. Box Two shows the results: t' is the elapsed time recorded by A. t is the elapsed time as recorded by the two B clocks. The equation in the center of Box Two describes the mathematical relationship between t' and t.

Box One

B_2

B_1

A

Box Two

v

$$t' = t\sqrt{1 - v^2}$$

t' A

t B_2

B_1

A

Lecture Eight—Transcript
Uncommon Sense: Stretching Time

In the preceding lecture I equipped you with this very high precision clock and this precision meter stick. And I equipped myself with a pair of them also—from the same manufacturer; they're identical. I sat on the roadside. And I put you, first, in a car moving at 70 miles an hour, and then I put you in an airplane moving at 600 miles an hour, and then I put you in a spacecraft moving past me at half the speed of light. And we applied the principle of relativity to this situation. And we asked, what would happen if each of us measured the speed of the same pulse of light that happened to come from a traffic signal, but could have come from anywhere else, and we arrived at the conclusion that seems absurd to us—that we, in all those situations, measured identically the same speed for light. Even though you and I were moving relative to each other, at one point at half the speed of light. Nevertheless, with our identical clocks and meter sticks, we reached the same conclusion for the speed of light— 299,792,458 meters per second. Period. No discrepancies.

The fact of your motion relative to me made absolutely no difference. Why? Because we agree that the laws of physics are the same in all uniformly moving reference frames. That's all special relativity says. And if that's true, one consequence of the laws of physics, the laws of electromagnetism in particular, is that there should be electromagnetic waves and they should move at speed c. That's what light waves are, and, therefore, we all have to get the same value for the speed of light.

But, how can it possibly be? How can it be that if you move past me at half the speed of light, and we measure the speed for the same light beam, that we get the same value when you're moving relative to me at such a high speed? It violates everything we know from our common sense. How can it possibly be?

Well, it seems absurd, actually, for one particular reason—because it violates our common sense. And now I want to insult all of my audience. The Teaching Company audiences tend to be a fairly sophisticated lot. But you're actually very provincial. You may think yourself a world traveler and have been all over the place, but you've spent all your time basically crawling around at relatively slow speeds. The fastest you've ever gone is 600 miles an hour in a commercial jet. Maybe a few of you have gone supersonically in the Concorde or a military plane or some thing. The fastest you've gone, maybe, at most, is a couple thousand miles an hour, relative to this hunk of rock that we call planet Earth. That is our home.

You have very little or no experience of moving at high speeds relative to anything that seems to be significant to your life. So you have a very limited provincial experience of the range of possible activities that are in this universe, including moving relative to things that are important to you at high speeds. Now, I have to put in a little parenthetical remark here. You actually do move at speeds close to the speed of light relative to some things. They are just things that aren't particularly important in your life. For example, we've been talking throughout the course about that distant planet in that distant galaxy that happens to be moving away from us at 80 percent of the speed of light. Relative to that, you are moving at 80 percent of the speed of light. And if you had business to communicate with the beings on that planet, you would certainly have to take relativity into account. You move at the speed of light relative to cosmic rays, which are coming toward Earth at 0.99999 the speed of light. They don't play a major role in your life. You hardly know about them. But, if they did, you would have to take in to account relativity. And it would be much more obvious to you.

When you're sitting watching this course on video, for example, the electrons that paint the picture on your TV screen are coming at you from the back of the TV tube at about 30 percent of the speed of light. Relative to them, you're moving at 30 percent of the speed of light. That's not a huge speed, compared to light. But it's significant. It doesn't affect you because you don't think about those electrons when you watch TV, but the engineer who designed your TV picture tube sure had to take relativity into account or otherwise the TV picture would be out of focus.

So there are people in the world for whom motion at speeds near that of light is important. An astrophysicist studying that distant galaxy does have to take relativity into account. An engineer designing that TV tube does have to take relativity into account. A cosmic-ray physicist does have to take relativity into account.

Now, where did our common sense come from? Well, think about how we developed our notions of time and space. When you were a baby and were crawling around, you began to get a sense of what space meant. What it meant to get from one place to another. When you were a little kid and you were sitting in the back of the car on a long trip and saying, "Daddy, are we there yet?", you were beginning to develop a sense of time. And that sense of time and space that you developed were coming out of that very limited, provincial experience of, as I say, crawling. And I use that term to mean moving slowly compared to the speed of light. Even 2,000 miles an hour in a supersonic airplane is far, far, far slower than the speed of light. You crawl around on this hunk of rock, and that is your limited experience.

I would assert that if you had grown up able to crawl at 90 percent of the speed of light, relativity would have been obvious to you. You wouldn't need this course. Nobody would need to go to school to study relativity, it would be intuitively obvious to us. If we were beings that were somehow based in interstellar gas clouds or something, as a science fiction novel by Fred Hoyle once described, and we tended to move around the universe at speeds near the speed of light all the time, then relativity would be intuitively obvious to us. It would be our common sense. The reason it's not common sense is simply because it's not in our everyday experience.

In order to appreciate relativity and to appreciate the richness of a universe in which the relativity principle holds, I'm going to have to ask you to suspend common sense. It's a very difficult thing to do. I'm not going to ask you to give up common sense entirely, although I'm going to ask you to expand on it. To enlarge the possibilities. That's what relativity asks us to do. And I think it's remarkable that this very simple principle—that the laws of physics are the same in all uniformly moving frames of reference, it sounds very benign—is so immediately at such odds with our common sense. But it is. And it is for the reason, again, that our common sense is built out of very limited experience. If you can abandon or at least agree to stretch your notion of common sense, then you're going to encounter the richer universe that relativity offers us.

Now let me make very clear, common sense isn't wrong. If it were wrong, common sense wouldn't tell us how to throw a tennis ball, or drive a car, or do many of the other "physics experiments" that we do here on planet Earth all the time and do very successfully. It's not that our common sense is wrong. It's that our common sense is limited. Newtonian physics, if you will, is the physics of common sense. It was built on our common sense notions of space and time. Those notions proved to be limited. Relativity tells us that, and the example from the last lecture of you whizzing by me in a spaceship at half the speed of light and are still both measuring the same speed for that light, that tells us that our common sense notions of space and time simply have to be wrong.

But when the relative speeds involved in our lives are small compared with c, small compared with the speed of light, then our common sense notions are good enough. They're not perfect. Even me pacing very slowly around this room, there are slight differences in space and time for me than for you because of my motion relative to you. These effects are so small that they're essentially negligible in our everyday lives. Even when you're traveling in a jet airplane at 600 miles an hour, or in a supersonic plane at 2,000 miles an hour, or even in an orbiting satellite going at 25,000 miles an hour, 17,000 miles an hour, 25,000 miles an hour on the way to the moon, these effects are very, very, very small. They're measurable. And there are a few instances—one of which is the global positioning system of satellites, which I'll talk about a little bit later in the course—where relativistic effects, even at the kind of speeds we use in everyday space travel or even airplane travel, have measurable, relativistic effects. But for most of us, those are completely negligible.

So there's nothing wrong with our common sense. It's just very limited. In fact, mathematically, if you take the equations of relativity and you reduce all velocities to something much, much smaller than c, then those equations reduce to the ordinary equations of physics that we knew about before relativity. So common sense isn't wrong. It's just limited. And what I'm doing here is asking you to expand your common sense.

I'm going to also ask you to watch your language. And this is a plea, not only to you in my audience, but also to some of my fellow teachers of relativity, because it's very easy to make statements that violate the spirit of the relativity principle. You've heard about political correctness on our campuses. You have to make statements that are in tune with the prevailing political norms. Well, I don't want to get into that. But I do want to ask you, and ask myself, and ask my fellow teachers of relativity to be relativistically correct in our language. And what that means is when you're describing what happens to space and time, be very careful to avoid any statements that might suggest there is a preferred frame of reference. A preferred state of motion. Why? Because there isn't a preferred frame of reference, and there isn't a preferred state of motion.

The Copernican principle has been expanded, through special relativity, to say that all uniformly moving frames of reference are equally valid places, situations to do physics. So, avoid any statements that would suggest anything to the contrary.

For example, in the last lecture, when we put you in first the car, then the airplane, and then the spaceship, and we said, well, we both measure the same speed for light, and we said how could that possibly be? And I simply hinted at the end of the lecture that it must mean that something is different about our measures of space and time.

You might jump to the conclusion that, well, maybe the meter stick in the moving vehicle shrinks. Maybe something funny happens to the clock in the moving vehicle because the vehicle is moving. That's sort of the philosophy that Lorentz and Fitzgerald had when they suggested, maybe the apparatus, the Michelson-Morley apparatus, contracts in the direction of motion. It's really this long, but because it's moving, it got contracted.

What's wrong with a statement like that? What's wrong with a statement like that is the sense that somebody is moving and somebody isn't. Somebody, probably you think the person on Earth, has the right to assert that they are at rest, and funny things are happening to clocks and meter sticks and space and time for the people who are moving. Nonsense. You, in the moving spacecraft moving relative to me; you, in the airplane moving past me at 600 miles an hour; you, in the car moving past me at 70 miles an hour—because those motions are uniform, you have every bit as much right to claim that you're a place for doing physics. You have no more right to claim you're the right place than I do. We both have equal claim on doing physics and doing physics correctly. That's what the principle of relativity says.

So don't think funny things happen to clocks and meter sticks or space and time because things move. The phrase, because things move, is a relativistically incorrect phrase. You're allowed to say, I am moving relative to you. Or, that clock is moving relative to this clock that I'm looking at. But you're not allowed to say that clock is moving and this one isn't and, therefore, funny things happen to that clock. That violates, directly, the spirit of the principle of relativity, which says all uniformly moving frames of reference are equally good places to do physics.

And that means any uniformly moving clock keeps time just as well as any other uniformly moving clock. It's just as accurate. Clocks don't become inaccurate "because they move." Because no uniformly moving clock has the right to say, "I'm at rest and all the other ones are moving." What may be the case, and, in fact, is the case, is that different clocks moving relative to each other keep different time. But, there's not one of them that can say, I keep the right time and all the rest of you are wrong, because you're "moving." Because nobody has the right to say, I am moving.

I will even slip occasionally and use phrases that are not correct. If I ever say the moving clock, or this is moving, what I really mean is, this is moving relative to that. That's why it's a relativity theory. It says only relative motion matters. Lecture Three we went over this with the Galilean relativity principle. Only relative motion matters. Statements about absolute motion are meaningless. They were in mechanics all along. They became so in all of physics with Einstein's special relativity. So everybody who's in uniform motion is in equally good motion to do physics.

So let's now move on and see what actually happens to space and time in special relativity. We'll start with time. We're going to be talking a lot in the next few lectures about events. I just want to tell you what an event is so we make it very clear. An event is something specified by giving both its place and its time. For example, your birth is an event. It occurred at a specific place, and it occurred at a specific time. Just to give the place, to say, New York City, for example, is not sufficient to specify your birth. Just to give a year, 1960, is not sufficient to specify your birth. New York, 1960, that does it. An event is a place and a time. And events are the key things in relativity. So we're going to talk a lot about events.

What I'm going to do now is give you a somewhat artificial seeming example that I hope will convince you of what exactly happens to time because of the principle of relativity being true. I'm going to imagine a device, which I'll call a light clock. And here's a picture of a light clock. And you audio people have a picture of the light clock in your booklet. The light clock consists of a box. Just a simple box.

At one end of the box is a light source. And at the other end of the box is a mirror. And we're going to imagine a pulse of light leaves the light source. Travels to the mirror. Reflects off the mirror. And comes back. And we're going to be interested in the time interval between two events. And those two events are the departure of the light pulse from the light source and the return of the light pulse back to the light source after it's bounced off the mirror.

If you will, this device is a clock, and that's the fundamental ticking. Tick as the light goes up, tock as it comes back. There's one period of the clock. And it keeps doing that. But we're just going to focus on one tick-tock of the clock. One outgoing light pulse hitting the mirror, coming back to the light source again. And the two events are: light pulse leaves the source, light pulse returns to the source. We want to know what the time interval is between those two events.

So, here's our light clock. Now, whenever you see pictures in relativity books or in my course or in anything dealing with relativity, it's crucial to ask yourself, and it's crucial to understand the answer to the question: In what frame of reference is this picture being drawn? Many relativity books fall down, I think, because they fail to tell you that. Or sometimes worse, they'll draw pictures that are ambiguous. They're partly from one frame of reference and partly from another. And in relativity, things tend to look different in different frames of reference. And it's important to catch that difference. And I'll try to do the best I can. Sometimes I'll slip, but I want to tell you, whenever possible, what frame of reference I'm dealing with.

So the picture I'm showing you right now on the left side of the screen is a picture drawn in a frame of reference at rest with respect to the light clock. What that means is we're in a frame of reference, we put this light box or light clock here, and it's at rest with respect to us. That's what I mean by saying this is a picture drawn in a frame of reference in which the light clock is at rest or, equivalently, a frame of reference at rest with respect to the light clock. And I'm assuming that I've got a uniformly moving frame of reference.

You might say, well, maybe it's at rest. Well, maybe it is at rest, but being at rest is meaningless. Maybe it's at rest on Earth. That's a particular state of uniform motion. Maybe it's at rest on Mars. Maybe it's whizzing through space at 99 percent of the speed of light relative to Earth. But as long as it's moving uniformly, that's an okay frame of reference. So, I don't know exactly what the light clock is doing relative to Earth. Doesn't matter. The point is I'm drawing a picture here from a frame of reference in which the light clock is at rest.

And in that frame of reference, here's what's going to happen. The light is going to leave the source. It's going to go up and hit the mirror. It's going to return to the source. It's all that happens. And the light is going to travel a total distance, which is twice the length of the box. And that's all we need to know at this point. What's the length of the light path for that light? It leaves the source. It travels up to the mirror. It reflects off the mirror; it comes back and hits the source. And we know how far it traveled. It traveled twice the length of the box. No problem.

Now, there are certainly plenty of other frames of reference that aren't at rest with respect to the light clock or light box equivalently through which the light clock is moving. If I am at rest with respect to the light clock and you go by me at 70 miles an hour in the car, then relative to you, the light clock is, in fact, moving. In fact, suppose you go by me in that direction. Then, judged from your frame of reference, the light clock is moving in the other direction relative to you. And you might say, oh, but it's really at rest. Uh-uh. That's not relativistically correct. Both of those frames of reference are equally valid because they're both uniformly moving frames of reference. And no one has the right to claim they are at rest or not.

So, is the light clock at rest or not? It is in one frame of reference. It isn't in another. And that's just the way it is. And that's O.K.

So let's look at that second frame of reference and see what happens. We'll look at the same situation. The light clock, the emission of the light—that's the first event—bounces off the mirror, comes back to the source—that's the second event. We're going to look at that sequence of events, at those two events in a frame of reference now in which the light clock is moving to the right. That means, relative to the frame in which the light clock is at rest. That frame is moving to the left. And, therefore, the light clock looks like it's moving to the right. It is moving to the right in that frame.

By the way, a word to avoid. You might want to say, "But isn't it really at rest?" Avoid the word "really" in relativity. It's a very, very dangerous word. Because really implies there's some special case, some special frame of reference in which things are really the case, which they're really right. The time is really this time. The length is really this length. This event really happened before this event. Uh-uh. To use the word "really" is to sort of pin a specialness on one frame of reference. So let's avoid that.

So here we are, simply in a different frame of reference, a different place. A different state of motion that is equally valid for doing physics. It's a frame of reference, which happens to be moving to the left, relative to the first frame of reference I discussed—the one in which the light clock was at rest. And so, in this new frame of reference, the light clock itself is moving to the right.

So it starts out. There it is. And I'll make a little arrow to show that it's moving to the right at some speed. And to make this make any sense, that speed is probably pretty significant compared to the speed of light. We already expect that because we know that these relativistic effects aren't important at very slow speeds. You won't see these effects if you do this experiment and move the light clock at 70 miles an hour or 600 miles an hour. But if you move it at 80 percent of the speed of light, this will be a big effect.

So, what happens? The light flash leaves the source and it travels straight to the mirror. But in this frame of reference straight to the mirror means it travels like that. At an angle. At the time the light pulse hits the mirror, the mirror is in a different location. The light pulse still hits the middle of the mirror. The same physical things have to happen. In one frame of reference, the light pulse left the source, it hit the middle of the mirror, and it came back. That's got to happen in the other frame of reference. There's no question about what happens. It's a question of interpretation, about how long the intervals are between what happens, and so on. So, here we are half way through the process. The light pulse has hit the upper mirror. It's in the process of reflecting off it. It comes back. And by the time it returns to the source, the light box is in a different place. And there is nothing funny and relativistic yet. I could have described this all in old-fashioned classical terms. The light clock could be in a car, which happens to be moving to the right. And the first frame of reference is the frame of reference of the car. And the second frame of reference is the frame of reference of an observer on the road who sees the car go by. And there's nothing unusual about this. These are two different descriptions of the same sequence of events from two different points of view. Two different frames of reference.

Here's the crucial point. In the second frame of reference, the one in which the light box is moving, notice the light path. The light path is longer. Why is it longer? It's longer because the light travels diagonally to get to the mirror, reflects, and comes back diagonally. It's a longer path. It still has the up and downness of the length of the box. But, in addition, it has a component of its motion in the direction the light box is going.

In classical physics, in old fashioned pre-relativistic physics, we say, oh well, that's okay because the light is actually moving a bit faster in the right-hand frame of reference, because it has the motion of the light box imposed on it. And we could describe that in terms of the ether and so on if we wanted.

But, now we believe in the principle of relativity. The principle of relativity says the laws of physics are the same for all observers in uniform motion, all laws of physics, including the laws of electromagnetism, including their predictions there are light waves, including the predictions that those light waves go at speed c. So, what has to be the case? The speed of the light has to be the same in both frames of reference. And, yet, in one frame of reference, the light is moving further than in the other frame of reference. This is where relativity comes in. Relativity comes in, in our assertion that the light moves at the same speed in both these frames of reference. That's what's going to give us all the trouble with time. That's what gave us the trouble in the experiment of measuring the speed of the light flash from the traffic light too, the assertion that all these observers had to measure the same speed. Observers in both these frames of reference measure the same speed for light. But in the left hand frame, in the frame of reference at rest with respect to the light clock, the path length is shorter. And we can conclude, in the left frame we have a shorter path; we've got the same speed; and, therefore, the time between the events is shorter.

In the frame of reference in which the light clock is moving to the right, we have a longer path. But by the principle of relativity we have exactly the same speed c for the light. And, therefore, it takes more time. And that's simply the way it has to be.

If you accept the principle of relativity—the very simple, benign-sounding principle that says the laws of physics, including electromagnetism and predictions about light, are the same in all frames of reference in uniform motion—then this conclusion has to follow: The time intervals between those two events are different in the two different frames of reference.

Now, you might say, oh, well, okay, this is just a peculiarity of this funny light clock we're using here. This is something that if I used a real clock, real clock, like this clock, that result wouldn't happen. But that's nonsense. We've made a clock. What's a clock? A clock is a device that accurately, repeatedly, undergoes some kind of happening that is periodic, that occurs over and over and over again. In an old pendulum clock, that could be the swing of a pendulum, once a second. In this light clock, it's the bouncing of the light pulse from the source back to the source. In this modern quartz clock, it's the fundamental vibration of a quartz crystal that vibrates 32,768 times per second. That's a power of two from one second. And then when you divide that down with electronic circuits you get a ticking every one second. Exactly 1.0000 seconds. A clock is simply a device that undergoes a repetitive, periodic motion or change of some kind. And that light clock is a perfectly good clock.

And what we are doing here is discovering, not something about the light clock, or not something even about light, but something about time. The phenomenon we've described here is called *time dilation*. Time is different in different frames of reference. Clocks do not keep the same time when they are moving relative to each other. They're still perfectly good clocks. There is nothing wrong with the light box when it's moving. It's the same one. It's just looked at from a different frame of reference. It isn't keeping bad time "because it's moving." It is keeping perfectly good time in either frame of reference. It's just keeping different time.

Time dilation isn't about light. It isn't about light clocks. It's about time itself. Measures of time are simply different for different observers in relative motion. The time interval between two events is not an absolute quantity. It's something that depends on your point of view. We're going to have to give up the absoluteness of time, and soon, the absoluteness of space if we accept the simple principle that the laws of physics are the same for all observers in uniform motion.

When you read books about relativity, you often hear time dilation described by saying, "moving clocks run slow." There are two things wrong with that. It's probably grammatically incorrect. It should say slowly. But much more profoundly, it's simply not relativistically correct. And I'd like you to pause right now; turn off your VCR; turn off your cassette player for just a minute and think about what is wrong with the statement: Moving clocks run slow. Why is that statement not relativistically correct? Think about that for a few minutes. When you're done thinking about it, start up again and we'll continue.

So, what's wrong with the statement: Moving clocks run slow? It implies there's something special about motion, special about movement, that there's somebody who's not moving, for whom the clock is right and doesn't run slow, and somebody else for whom, because they're moving, the clock runs slow. Nonsense. Nobody can say, I'm moving and you're not, or, you're moving and I'm not. That's the whole point of relativity. Moving clocks run slow is an absurd statement. It's nevertheless used very commonly, including in physics books or books for non-science people about relativity, to describe this phenomenon of time dilation.

One problem with the idea of moving clocks run slow is you might imagine yourself in a spacecraft whizzing past Earth with a clock. That's a moving clock. Right? And the moving clock runs slow So you might imagine, in your frame of reference everything seems to have slowed down. You watch the hands of your clock creeping slowly. And your heart beats slowly. Nonsense. That frame of reference is just as good a frame of reference for doing physics in as any other frame of reference. Things have to seem perfectly normal in that frame of reference. If they didn't seem perfectly normal in that frame of reference, physics would be somehow different there. And the whole point of relativity is the laws that govern physical reality don't depend on your state of motion. They are the same for all observers in uniform motion. Things can't seem strange even if you're in a spacecraft whizzing along at 0.99999 the speed of light. Everything in the context of that spacecraft, in your frame of reference—your heartbeat, your aging—all that seems perfectly normal. Time, for you, may be running differently than it does on Earth. We'll get to that in the next lecture. But everything seems perfectly normal.

So, what does time dilation really say? Let me describe what it says. Here's what it really says. It doesn't say moving clocks run slow. Instead it says something a little more complicated. It says, if I have two events, and I measure the time between them on a clock that is present at both events—remember the light clock when it was in the frame of reference where it was at rest, that light clock, that same box, was present at the emission and the return of the light flash. We are going to now replace that light box with a couple of real clocks. And so what does it say? It says something like this: It says, first of all we are not going to say moving clocks run slow anymore. That's bad. Relativistically incorrect. We're going to say, a little more sophisticatedly, the time between two events is shorter when you measure it with one single clock that's present at both events, rather than measured by two different clocks.

So here's the picture. This is the picture that should come to your mind when you think about time dilation. I've got two clocks—clock B-1 and clock B-2. And they're located at two different places. And I've got another clock—clock A—whose state of motion relative to the other two clocks is such that A will be present at clock B-1, and then later it will be present at clock B-2. And the two events we're interested in are the first event, which is shown here, when clock A passes clock B-1, and the second event, which will be when clock A passes clock B-2.

Now you may be very tempted to say, oh, A is the clock that's moving. And I've got an arrow, showing that, indeed, A is the clock that is moving. And later, clock A will be above clock B-2. And in that sense, it is moving—in the frame of reference of the clocks B-1 and B-2. And that's the frame of reference from which this picture is drawn. Remember, I asked you to always think about what frame of reference is the picture shown in. That frame of reference, clock A is indeed moving. But that doesn't say clock A is absolutely moving. It simply says clock A is moving relative to the frame of reference in which the two clocks B are at rest. They are at rest relative to some frame of reference. The one in which they're at rest. They are at rest relative to each other. I put them that way. I've glued them to the wall in that frame of reference. Clock A is moving relative to that frame of reference, but clock A isn't moving absolutely.

Clock A has every right to say, "Oh, the clocks B are moving relative to me, I'm not moving." So, that's why I don't want to call clock A the moving clock. Clock A is simply a clock that happens to be present at the two events. It's a single clock. Clock A is present at the event of clock A and clock B-1 coinciding. And clock A is present at the event of clock A and clock B-2 coinciding. Neither clock B1 nor clock B-2 is present at both those events.

And what does time dilation say? Time dilation says that the time elapsed on clock A between those two events will be less than the time as measured by the two other clocks. And that is crucial. It takes two clocks in one of the frames of reference, and only one clock in the other frame of reference to do this measurement—to determine the time interval between the two events.

Now, this is not a mathematically oriented course, but I do want to tell you the actual result of doing this measurement and calculating what the time differences should be. There is a little formula. And we will use this occasionally. And any of you who have had high school algebra and can use the Pythagorean theorem could easily go back to the light clock picture and look at those diagonals. Hint: Diagonals have to do with the Pythagorean theorem. And you could calculate the time in the one frame versus the time in the other frame.

And you would find that the time, which I will call t prime (t'), that's the little thing after the t for time on the left side of that equation. The thing I call t prime, that's the time measured on clock A, the one clock that's present at both events. That time is the time measured on the other two clocks multiplied by a factor 1 minus v squared, square rooted, where v is the speed measured in terms in the speed of light. So if you're going half the speed of light, v is a half. And that number is always smaller than one, and, therefore, t prime is always less than t. And we're left with the conclusion that time is simply not an absolute quantity. The time interval between two events is relative. It depends on your frame of reference.

Lecture Nine

Muons and Time-Traveling Twins

Scope:

Experiments with subatomic particles called muons dramatically confirm that time dilation really occurs. These particles are produced in the upper atmosphere and travel downward at nearly the speed of light. But they're radioactive, and they decay in such a short time that they shouldn't last long enough to make it to the ground. Yet they do—showing that time runs slower in the muons' frame of reference by just the amount expected from time dilation. A more dramatic example of time dilation would occur if we had spaceship capable of achieving speeds, relative to Earth, near that of light. Suppose one of two twins leaves Earth on such a spaceship, travels to a distant star, and returns. Each leg of the trip is like the journey of the third clock in the previous lecture, showing that less time elapses on the spaceship than back on Earth. The traveling twin returns younger!

Why can't the traveling twin argue the same for Earth—that from her point of view, her stay-at-home brother moves away on a distant journey and returns and should, therefore, be younger? Because the situation isn't symmetric: The Earthbound twin stays in essentially uniform motion, while the traveling twin makes an abrupt turnaround at the distant star. The traveling twin doesn't stay in uniform motion the whole time, while the Earthbound twin does. The traveling twin occupies two different uniformly moving reference frames, separated by the turnaround; while the Earthbound twin remains in one reference frame.

The twins' experiment actually has been done, but with an atomic clock flown around the Earth. It registers slightly less elapsed time than a clock remaining on Earth—but the difference is small because the aircraft's speed is so small compared with c.

Outline

I. An experimental verification of time dilation.

    A. Muons are subatomic particles produced by cosmic rays high in Earth's atmosphere.

        1. They rain down on Earth at a steady rate and can, therefore, be considered "clocks."

        2. The muons are radioactive and decay in a time so short that very few should be expected to reach sea level.

    B. In the 1950s, physicists measured the number of muons arriving each hour atop Mount Washington in New Hampshire; it was about 600 per hour.

        1. These muons were moving at $0.994c$ and, even at that high speed, their radioactive decay meant that only about 25 should survive to sea level.

        2. But a measurement at sea level revealed about 400 muons each hour. This is consistent with time in the muons' frame passing at about 1/9 the rate it does on Earth. Work out the quantity $\sqrt{1-0.994^2}$ and you will see that it is just about 1/9. So time dilation really happens!

    C. Another example: Suppose we had a spaceship capable of $0.8c$ relative to Earth. It sets out on a trip to a star 10 light-years distant (one light-year is the distance light travels in a year, so the speed of light is simply 1 light-year/year).

        1. From the Earth's point of view, the ship is going 10 light-years at 0.8 light-years/year. Because distance = speed x time, the time this takes is $t = 10$ ly $/ 0.8$ ly per year $= 12.5$ years.

        2. But according to time dilation, the time on the ship is:
$$t' = (12.5 \text{ years}) \times \sqrt{1-0.8^2} = (12.5 \text{ years}) \times (0.6) = 7.5 \text{ years}$$

II. The "Twins Paradox": a famous seeming paradox of relativity.

   A. Imagine the same star trip, but now the ship turns around once it reaches the star. The return trip is just like the outbound trip, so it takes 12.5 years according to observers on Earth and 7.5 years in the ship. When the traveling twin returns, she is 15 years older, but her brother is 25 years older!

   B. The paradox: Why can't the traveling twin consider that she's at rest and that Earth goes away on a 10-light-year journey at $0.8c$, in which case she should conclude that her brother will be younger? Answer: The situation is not symmetric.

   1. The Earthbound twin stays all the time in a single, uniformly moving reference frame (here we neglect the nonuniform motion associated with Earth's rotation and orbital motion; because these are slow compared with c, they don't have a significant effect on the results).

   2. The traveling twin occupies two different uniformly moving reference frames, going in opposite directions. They're separated by the ship's turnaround. The traveling twin feels that turnaround; Earth doesn't. The situation really is different for the two twins, so there's no paradox.

   3. Think about what's *special* about special relativity: It is restricted to frames of reference in *uniform* motion. The statement "I am moving" is meaningless according to the principle of relativity, but the statement "my motion changed" is meaningful. Here, the traveling twin can rightly say "my motion changed," but the Earthbound twin cannot.

   C. By going faster, the traveling twin could make her trip time arbitrarily small; as v approaches the speed of light c (or v approaches 1 in our formula), the time-dilation factor $\sqrt{1 - v^2}$ approaches 0. If she goes at very nearly c, the trip will take just barely over 25 years' Earth time, but a negligibly small amount of ship time—so she will return 25 years younger than her twin.

   D. By going farther, the traveling twin can go further into the future.

1. Suppose she goes to the Andromeda galaxy, 2 million light-years distant, at nearly c.
2. The shortest Earth time a round trip can take is just over 4 million years, but the ship time can be arbitrarily small. So she can return to Earth 4 million years in the future.
3. But this is a one-way trip! If the traveling twin does not like what she finds, there is no going back! Time travel to the past is not permitted.

E. Can we hope to duplicate the twin's trip? Not with today's spacecraft.
   1. Scientists have sent an atomic clock on a round-the-world airplane trip. On return, it read less time—by some 300 nanoseconds (300 billionths of a second)—than its stay-behind twin.
   2. The effect is clearly measurable but hardly dramatic, because the airplane's speed is so much less than that of light.
   3. This experiment actually involves effects of both special and general relativity, as we'll see in subsequent lectures.

Essential Reading:

Mook and Vargish, *Inside Relativity*, Chapter 4, pp. 110–111.

Hoffmann, *Relativity and Its Roots*, Chapter 5, pp. 109–110.

Hey and Walters, *Einstein's Mirror*, Chapter 3, pp. 64–66.

Suggested Reading:

Fritzsch, *An Equation that Changed the World*, Chapter 11.

Moore, *A Traveler's Guide to Spacetime*, Sections 4.7.3 and 5.8.

Taylor and Wheeler, *Spacetime Physics*, 2nd edition, Chapter 4.

Davies, *About Time: Einstein's Unfinished Revolution*, Chapter 2.

Hafele and Keating, "Around-the-World Atomic Clocks: Predicted Relativistic Time Gains" and "Around-the-World Atomic Clocks: Observed Relativistic Time Gains," *Science*, vol. 177, pp. 166–170 (July 1972).

Questions to Consider:

1. Suppose two triplets leave Earth at the same time and undertake roundtrip space journeys of identical length and at the same speed but in opposite directions. When they return, will they be the same age or will one be older? How will their ages compare with their third sibling, who stayed at home on Earth?

2. In 1999, scientists discovered a planetary system orbiting a star 44 light-years from Earth. How far into the future could you travel by taking a high-speed trip to this star and returning immediately back to Earth? Under what conditions would you achieve this maximum future travel? How long would you judge the trip to take?

3. Suppose the twin in the spaceship traveled at $0.6c$ instead of $0.8c$. By how much would the twins' ages differ when the traveling twin returns to Earth?

Time Dilation : An Experiment with Muons

In this experiment subatomic particles called muons, which have a fixed rate of decay, stream down from high in the atmosphere toward earth at a speed of 0.994c. The experiment has two stations, one at the top and one at the bottom of the mountain, that measure the number of muons passing by.

In the first box, we see the results that would be expected if time dilation did not occur. As the muons stream down toward earth, many are detected at the top of the mountain in the first station. But since muons decay at such a rapid rate, the expected count of muons passing the second station at the bottom of the mountain is dramatically lower.

In the second box we see the results as they actually do occur, with time dilation affecting the results. Since the muons are traveling at a significant fraction of the speed of light (0.994c), their measure of elapsed time is significantly slower than the time recorded by the two stations. Thus, with the muons' time running more slowly, most of them do indeed reach the second station.

A Little Math...

Distance = speed × time, so in Earth-star frame of reference, trip takes:

$$t = \frac{d}{v} = \frac{10 \text{ light-years}}{0.8 \text{ light-years / year}} = 12.5 \text{ years}$$

Time dilation: $t' = t\sqrt{1-v^2}$, so in ship frame, trip takes:

$$t' = (12.5 \text{ years}) \sqrt{1-0.8^2}$$
$$= (12.5 \text{ years}) (0.6) = 7.5 \text{ years}$$

Star Trip!

In this diagram, we see what kind of strange effects time dilation can have. A twin on a spaceship traveling at 0.8c is making a round trip journey from Earth to a nearby star and back. The other twin remains behind on Earth. On the initial trip to the star, the twin on the spaceship experiences a time lapse of 7.5 years while the twin on Earth experiences an elapsed time of 12.5 years.

0.8c

Ship time: 7.5 years

Earth/star time: 12.5 years

Start

10 light-years

Initial trip to the star from Earth

Turn around

0.8c

Ship time: 15 years

Earth/star time: 25 years

10 light-years

Total round trip

On the return trip, the twin in the spaceship experiences another 7.5 years of elapsed time for a total elapsed time of 15 years, and the twin on Earth experiences another 12.5 years of elapsed time for a total elapsed time of 25 years. The twin in the rocketship returns 10 years younger than the twin who remained on Earth!

Lecture Nine—Transcript
Muons and Time-Traveling Twins

Welcome to Lecture Nine: "Muons and Time-Traveling Twins." In the previous lecture, I introduced you to this notion of time dilation. The idea that the time interval between two events depends on your frame of reference. Time is no longer an absolute. And we did the time dilation experiment by thinking about a special device, a light clock. But we concluded from that, that this was really a property of time itself. Time is simply not an absolute quantity. Different observers measure different time intervals between the same pairs of events. And we described in some detail—with a pair of clocks in one frame of reference and another clock that moved between one clock and the other—exactly what it meant to say that time was different in one frame of reference than another frame of reference.

Measures of time between two events simply are not absolute. Now, I grant that you probably have great difficulty accepting this intuitively, because all your experience suggests that to say this class is one hour long, or this lecture is a half hour long, or this airplane flight is two hours long, that that has an absolute meaning. It doesn't. To say that the time between your birth and your sitting here is 40 years or whatever, that is not an absolute statement either. In different frames of reference, different observers will judge different time intervals for the time difference between those two events. Time is simply not an absolute.

If you have trouble accepting that, on the other hand I hope you don't have trouble accepting Einstein's principle that the laws of physics are the same for all observers in uniform motion. That all frames of reference in uniform motion are equally good places for doing physics. If you accept that—the logic I applied last time showing that this light path from the light being emitted by a source in that light clock to the return to that source, that the path was different in two different frames of reference—but if you believe relativity, you believe that light goes at speed c in all reference frames and that led us immediately to the conclusion that the time intervals between those events were different in different frames of reference.

And I can't emphasize enough that this is not a property that is peculiar to that device I used in the previous lecture. The light clock.

It's not even peculiar to clocks at all. All measures of time, all processes, physiological processes, biological processes, chemical reactions, physical processes, all processes that measure time in any way are affected in exactly the same way, because this is not something that happens and drags back the hands of clocks and slows them down. This is time itself that's different in different frames of reference. Don't look for some mechanical thing that slows down the clocks because they're "moving." That would be a relativistically incorrect statement to make. It's simply that measures of time are different in different frames of reference. Time is not an absolute.

Some things are absolutes, by the way. Relativity is not the theory that says everything is relative, nothing has any absoluteness. Nonsense. There are things that are absolute. The laws of physics are the same for all observers in all frames of reference. The speed of light, as a consequence, is the same for all observers in all frames of reference.

But some things that we used to think of as absolutes and applying to everybody, particularly measures of time and, as we'll see soon, of space, are not absolutes.

Well, does this really happen? Does time dilation really occur? We sure don't notice it when we drive around. If I jump in my car in New York and drive to San Francisco and I compare my clock when I get to San Francisco with the clock that's there, that was synchronized with the clock in New York when I left, I'll hardly notice the difference. In fact, I won't notice the difference unless it's a super accurate atomic clock. And then I might notice a few billionths of a second difference. These effects are negligible in our everyday lives.

But there are situations in which they become completely obvious. And there are situations, eventually, maybe involving interstellar space travel, where we could put them to advantage. Let me give you an example of an experiment. This experiment was done in the 1950s with the particular goal of, not only testing, but more, demonstrating the principle of time dilation. Demonstrating that special relativity is correct. By the time this experiment was done, there was no question about special relativity being correct. I mentioned before it's one of the most tested theories in all of physics. It's at the foundation of our understanding of physical reality. So, the experiment I'm going to describe is not the clincher that says, "Oh, Einstein was right." But it's an experiment that demonstrates, quite straightforwardly, that it had to be correct.

And the experiment involves some clocks. Now, what's a clock again? A clock is anything that regularly measures time intervals. And the clocks in this case are tiny subatomic particles called *muons*. And these muons are being created all the time in the upper atmosphere as high energy cosmic rays—which are themselves subatomic particles that originate sometimes in the sun and sometimes in the vastness of the cosmos in our galaxy, or maybe even outside it—and they come barreling through the universe at very, very high speeds. And when they slam into Earth's atmosphere, they cause all kinds of nuclear reactions to occur in the nuclei of the atoms they hit, and they produce different particles. And showers of particles are coming down through the upper atmosphere of the Earth all the time as these cosmic rays hit the upper atmosphere.

And among these particles are these subatomic particles called muons. And the muons are radioactive, as are many elementary particles. Not really elementary, because they break up into other particles. We'll say more about that much later in the course. But these particles are radioactive. And they decay. And they decay at a certain rate. And the rate of their decay is what we're going to use as a clock in this experiment. And we're going to demonstrate that these clocks, these muons, when they're moving relative to us at high speed, seem to decay more slowly than they would if they were at rest relative with us.

Now, "seem" is not quite a good word, because it implies there's something funny about their frame of reference. So let me change that to "do decay at a rate which is different than if they were at rest relative to us." So let me describe for you this experiment. The experiment was done on Mount Washington in New Hampshire. Mount Washington sticks up about 6,000 feet in to the atmosphere from sea level. And there is a rain of muons coming down due to these cosmic ray interactions high in the atmosphere. And the particular muons that were singled out for this experiment were muons that were moving at about 0.994 of the speed of light. That's 99.4 percent of the speed of light. That's pretty fast. Relativistic effects will be quite dramatic at speeds like that.

So here come these muons. And the scientists measure how many muons per hour were coming into a detector. A muon detector. A device that gave off a little flash of light whenever a muon came into that detector and disintegrated. They could tell how many muons were coming in. And the number of muons coming in to the detector was something like 600 every hour. At the top of the mountain there were a lot of muons coming into the detector.

Now, scientists can measure the lifetime of these muons. And when they stop one of the muons, or stop a bunch of the muons in their detector and they watch them decay, they can determine the rate at which the muon's internal clock is running. And they can conclude that even though these muons are traveling very, very rapidly—99.4 percent of the speed of light—they decay so fast that there should be very few of them left when you get to sea level. The prediction was that there might be about 25 or so when you get to sea level.

So here's the experiment. Muons come down on top of Mount Washington. You measure how many are coming down every hour into your muon detector. They're coming about 600 every hour. Pretty big number. You study these muons and see how fast they decay. Or maybe you just look up that information in a book, because the radioactive decay rates of these elementary particles are pretty well known. So you look up that quantity. Or you measure it by watching the muons decay and detecting them with Geiger counters and other radiation detectors. And you ask yourself, "Okay, if they're decaying at that rate, and they're moving at 0.994c, how many of them will decay between the top of the mountain and sea level?" And the answer comes out: Most of them will decay. And you'll expect, on the average, only about 25 to survive every hour.

So that's the essence of the experiment. It's kind of a statistical experiment. You count the muons present at the top of Mount Washington. You're then going to go down to sea level. There's a wonderful movie, by the way, made of this experiment. An old 1950s movie. And you see them moving all their apparatus down Mount Washington in leased trucks and setting it up again in Cambridge, Massachusetts, at MIT, essentially at sea level, to do the experiment all over again down there. And they carefully compensate for the thickness of the atmosphere, which affects the muons and things like that. And they get all that stuff right. And they set up the counters. And they expect to find 25 muons every hour if they don't believe in relativity. And, instead, what do they find? Well, they expect very few muons at sea level; what actually happens, actually most of the muons reach sea level. It's over 400 an hour.

Most of the muons have survived. Why? Their internal clocks that caused them to decay radioactively are keeping time at a certain rate. The muons decay at a certain rate. You expect it in the relatively short time—it's a few microseconds, a few millionths of a second— that it would take them to get from the top of Mount Washington to sea level, most of them would have decayed. How do you explain the fact that most of them didn't decay? Well, their internal clocks must have been keeping time at a different rate than the clocks in the laboratory—the clocks at rest with respect to Mount Washington, the clocks at rest with respect to the laboratory at sea level. That's the explanation for what's going on.

You'll remember I introduced the time dilation factor near the end of the last lecture. And this is about as mathematical as we're getting, and you don't need to worry about this too much. But, in fact, the time measured on the "moving clock of the muon," if I may use that expression—again, it's a relativistically incorrect expression—the time measured on the muon clock, that was my t prime. That's given by the time measured in the laboratory, by the clocks at rest with respect to Mount Washington, multiplied by the square root of 1 minus the speed squared, where the speed is given as a fraction of the speed of light. Well, 0.994 squared is about 0.99. And 1 minus that is about 0.01. So that's a very, very tiny number. It comes out be about a ninth. And what that says is moving at $0.994c$, the muons should be keeping time at one-ninth the rate of the clocks on Earth. And that is, in fact, completely consistent with the survival of about 400 muons to reach sea level instead of the 25 you would expect if the clocks, on the muons—their internal, radioactive, time-keeping mechanism—if that were running at the same rate of speed as the clocks in the laboratory.

So this is a fairly dramatic confirmation of time dilation. It really does occur. It's not the kind of satisfying demonstration you might like where I pick up a clock and run past you and show you time dilation that way. We can't do that yet. We can't move macroscopic objects at $0.994c$. But we have plenty of subatomic particles moving around at those speeds, and they very dramatically show time dilation. And this example illustrates that beautifully.

So there's an experiment that verifies that time dilation occurs. It really does happen. And it really would happen if we could pick up that clock and move it at speeds approaching that of light. In fact, it really does happen even if we move that clock in a jet airplane, as I'll describe later, it's just a rather insignificant effect.

But let me give you now an example of what would happen if we could move macroscopic, that is, big-sized objects like people in spaceships at speeds substantially like that of light. So, we're going to do an experiment, or "thought experiment" like Galileo and Einstein have done before us, we're going to do a thought experiment about a star trip. A trip to a distant star. And we're going to imagine we have a spaceship capable of traveling at say, 80 percent of the speed of light.

Now, it may be technologically not possible to do this, at least at this point in humanity's history. But there's nothing in the principles of physics that rules out what I'm about to describe. That's why it's a valid thought experiment. It's something we could imagine doing, and we believe we know what the outcome of the experiment would be because we understand the laws of physics.

So, we're going to do a star trip. And we're going to go from Earth to a star, which I'm going to say is 10 light years away from Earth. Now let me take a minute and explain what a light year is. I'm going to be measuring distances in the next few lectures in light years. Sometimes in light minutes. Sometimes in light seconds. This is a measure of distance, not of time, even though it's got the word year in it. It's a measure of distance.

What's a light year? A light year is the distance that light travels in one year. How big is that? It's trillions of miles. But I don't really care. It's 186,000 miles a second, times the number of seconds in a year, which is about 3.15 times—31 million, roughly. So multiply those out you'll figure out what it is. But I don't care what it is in real distance—it's a quarter of the way to the nearest star, approximately, if you want to get a feel for it. It's much bigger than the solar system, for example. That's not the point. The point is, it's a convenient measure of distance when you're talking about relativity and speeds near the speed of light, because what's the speed of light? Well, we know it is 186,000 miles a second. We know it is one foot per a billionth of a second. One foot per nanosecond. We know it is 300 million meters a second. But, what is it in light years per year. Think about that a second. A light year, by definition, is the distance light travels in one year. So what's the speed of light? Real simple. It's one light year per year. That makes all the mathematics, all the arithmetic, very easy.

So I'm going to deal with distances—not in miles or meters or centimeters or nanometers—I'm going to deal with distances in light years. Sometimes I'll talk about light minutes. For example, the sun is about eight light minutes from Earth. What does that mean? It means light from the sun times the time it leaves the sun until the time it gets to Earth takes about eight minutes. Jupiter, at least at some points in its orbit, is about half a light hour from Earth. What does that mean? It means it takes light 30 minutes—the duration of one of these lectures—to get from Earth to Jupiter; or a radio signal, which is also an electromagnetic wave like light, from the Galileo space probe out at Jupiter now going in orbit around that planet, takes about 30 minutes for the radio signals from that spacecraft to come back. The moon. The moon is about one and a quarter light seconds from Earth. Round trip transit time to talk to an astronaut on the moon is about two-and-a-half seconds.

You do a telephone conversation by a satellite and the satellites that carry those conversations are 22,000 miles up. There's a reason for that. They orbit the Earth in exactly 24 hours. The same as the Earth goes around. And they sit at one place above the Earth for that reason. That round trip is about 40,000 miles or a fraction of a light second. A foot is one light nanosecond. You get the idea.

We're going to measure distances in light time units. Light times time. And the light year is the appropriate unit for measuring interstellar distances. A light year is simply the distance light travels in one year.

So here we have this star trip. And going at the speed of light it would take, therefore, 10 years to get from the Earth to this star. We're going to go in a spacecraft, which I've hypothesized is technologically capable of achieving speeds of 80 percent of the speed of light—$0.8c$. So here we go. We're going to start out on this star trip at $0.8c$, and we're going to do a little math to figure out how we get there. Now, hold on. This is just arithmetic. It's the fifth grade formula, distance equals speed times time. And I want to apply it to that situation. No relativity here at all. Distance equals speed times time.

We know the distance. It's 10 light years. We know the speed. It's 0.8c or 0.8 light years per year, because the speed of light is one light year per year. So, distance—10 light years—equals speed—0.8 light years per year—times the time. We can figure out how long it's going to take.

By the way, I don't believe in doing math problems unless I sort of know the answer already. So I'm just going to think a little bit about the answer. I'm going at 0.8 the speed of light, 80 percent of the speed of light. If I were going at the speed of light, since that star is 10 light years away, it would take me 10 years. I'm going a little slower, so I expect an answer a little more than 10 years.

So let's do the math. Time is going to be the distance divided by the speed. That's 10 light years divided by 0.8 light years per year. And it all comes out nicely at 12-and-a-half years. So that's how long I'm going to say, from Earth, that that trip is going to take. It's going to take 12.5 years as I measure time on Earth.

But what about in the spaceship? Well, the situation is very similar to our time dilation experiments, especially the last visual I showed you in the last lecture where we had two clocks at rest with respect to each other, and another clock that moved from one to the other. The spaceship is carrying a clock—that's like the clock that's present at both events. The spaceship's clock is there when the spaceship passes Earth; it's there when the spaceship passes the star. We can imagine there are clocks on the Earth and star that are themselves synchronized together. And we've got a perfect time dilation situation. Exactly like we set up in the last lecture. And so, we can argue that the time on the spaceship is given by the time on Earth multiplied by that relativistic factor, the square root of one minus the speed squared, where the speed is measured in a fraction of the speed of light.

Again, if you don't like the arithmetic, don't worry about it. But it easily computes to give us the answer. Time dilation says t prime— the time in the ship's frame of reference—is the time in the Earth's frame of reference. And again, there's nothing special here about Earth. It's the fact that we have the two clocks in the Earth-star frame of reference. We're assuming the Earth and the star are pretty much at rest with respect to each other. Those two clocks versus the one clock carried by the ship.

So, we're going to just apply that formula, t, the Earth time, is 12.5 years. We're going to multiply it by the square root of one minus 0.8 squared. I chose those numbers for a particular reason—0.8 squared is 0.64. One minus 0.64—if you had change from it from a dollar for 64 cents, you'd get back 36 cents—0.36. The square root of 0.36 is 0.6. So that factor is 0.6, and it all comes out to 7.5 years.

So, if we look at the star trip, we start out at 0.8c. We travel to the star. Earth time that has elapsed is 12.5 years. Ship time that has elapsed is 7.5 years.

That's just the way it is. It's just like the muons. Here we're keeping time in the spaceship at a smaller rate—about 0.6 the rate we were on Earth. In the muon case, it was more dramatic, because they were going not at 0.8c, but 0.994c. So that's what would happen if we could do this experiment. Just exactly like the muon situation. Just exactly like the situations I set up in the last lecture.

You might ask me, does 7.5 years really elapse in the spaceship. Isn't it really 12 years? Suppose you're the pilot of the spaceship, what will you have experienced when you get to the star? Won't 12 years—really 12.5 years—won't you really be 12.5 years older? No, 7.5 years will have elapsed for you. Remember, we're not talking about clocks here. We're not talking about something dragging on the hands and slowing the clocks back because we're in a bad frame of reference. All these frames of reference are good.

What we're talking about is the measures of time are different in different reference frames—7.5 years really have elapsed for the time-traveling twin, or the traveling twin there in the spaceship.

So let's go back now and revisit that twin idea that I described in the very first lecture. It doesn't take much to do the twin experiment from where we are already. Already we've put one twin in a spaceship. She's traveled the 10 light year distance to the star. The Earth time that's elapsed is 12.5 years. In her ship, according to her ship clock, according to her physiological aging processes, according to everything else that involves time, 7.5 years have elapsed.

However, she's now 10 light years away, so it's a little bit hard to sort of look at her and compare. I mean, if she sends back a radio signal or a TV picture of herself, well we got to worry about the travel time for that light. And things get a little bit complicated. Let's turn her around, and let's bring her back right here on Earth where you, her twin, are sitting. And let's see what things look like then.

Then there's no ambiguity. You and the twin are right side by side. No question. Don't have to worry about time for light to get between you or radio signals or whatever. So let's turn this ship around. And let's head it back at 0.8c. Now, this is exactly the situation we just had, except instead of leaving Earth, we're leaving the star.

So we're going to head back at 0.8c, and how much time is going to elapse? Well, it's exactly the same situation we just had. The spaceship is carrying one clock moving between a clock on the star and a clock on the Earth. And, of course, it doesn't really matter whether there are clocks there or not. All manifestations of time exhibit this effect. So the ship is going to go back to Earth. There it is. And how much time has elapsed? Well, Earth-star time it was 12.5 years one way, so it's 25 years round trip. What about in the ship? Well, it was 7.5 years one way, so it's 15 years coming back. The twin hops out of the spaceship and he's 10 years younger than you are.

Can it be? Isn't this just something that happened to the clocks? But she's really experienced the same physiological wear and, tear on her body. No. She has experienced 15 years of time. And you have experienced 25 years of time. And you're standing right next to each other. And you're different. And you were twins. You still are twins. And yet you're 10 years apart.

Could it be? Is it possible? Yes, it is. And it could be. The reason this bothers a lot of people has to do with, first of all, it bothers you because you don't want time to do strange things like that. But even if you accept that time does strange things, then you may ask a more subtle question. You may say, wait a minute. You've been teaching me about everything being relative. Well, why can't the twin who jumps in the spaceship say, oh, here's what I see. I'm sitting in my spaceship. I see the Earth's going away at 80 percent of the speed of light, and that's a perfectly legitimate thing for her to say. And then I see the Earth turn around, and come back at 80 percent of the speed of light. And so why isn't my brother 10 years younger than I am?

Why don't 25 years elapse for me and 15 years for my brother? We can't have it both ways, because we're standing there side by side. And there is some objective truth to either, we're the same age, or one's older, or the other's older. So, who's right? Why can't I simply reciprocate? Why can't I do the same picture, except draw it from my point of view—the spaceship at rest, Earth zooms out 10 light years away, comes back, and the traveler on Earth should be younger. Why not?

This is what bothers people. Once they get beyond the notion that time gets messed up a little bit, you begin to accept that strange things are going to happen to time. Why isn't this reciprocal? Why doesn't it happen like that? Well, there's a subtlety here. And the subtlety is best understood if you remember what's special about the special theory of relativity. The special theory of relativity, special relativity, is special because it applies only to uniform motion. It says the statements about "I am moving" are meaningless. It's meaningless for me on Earth to say, oh, I'm at rest, but the twin in the spaceship is traveling. It's similarly meaningless, for the spaceship twin to say, I'm at rest and the Earth is traveling. Those are both equally meaningful and equally meaningless statements. Nobody has any authority to say, I'm at rest and you're moving.

However, in special relativity at least, although motion doesn't matter, uniform motion doesn't matter, changes in motion do matter, because special relativity applies only to uniformly moving reference frames. Remember what uniform motion is, way back from Galileo and Newton, it's motion in a straight line at constant speed. If you do any thing else—slow down and stop, speed up, change direction, turn around, go in a circle, turn around, that's what happened in this experiment—then that motion is no longer uniform. There really is an asymmetry in this situation. The two twins are not in the same situation, as far as special relativity is concerned. One twin, the one on Earth, is in uniform motion the entire time. The other twin, the one in the spaceship, is not in uniform motion the entire time. There's a small interval when she's turning around. During that interval, she feels great big forces. Just like if you turn a car very suddenly on a high-speed turn around a curve, you feel yourself thrown to the outside of the car. Or you sit in an airplane while it's accelerating down the runway and you feel yourself pushed back in the seat. The traveling twin feels forces like that when her spaceship turns around. Back on Earth, they don't feel those forces.

As far as special relativity is concerned, her motion has changed. And that's a real thing. That's an absolute. She can't say, I was moving and now I'm not moving. But she can say, my motion changed. And Earth's motion did not change. She's in two different frames of reference in this trip, she's in one frame of reference going out, and she's in a different frame of reference, a different state of motion, going back. There is no symmetry between the two. And so there is no problem with the fact that one twin comes back younger.

Now, you might think about this a little bit more, and I'm just going to give you hints of two answers to questions you might want to ask that I don't have time to go into in detail. This whole process can be treated from the point of view of general relativity, which treats completely arbitrary kinds of motion. And it gives the same result. You might ask, what happens if the twins try to communicate with each other as they're going? Well, basically, what happens is you will find that they can keep in touch with each other, and they can count up the number of signals each one sends back. Suppose one sends back a pulse or a message every year. You can count up those messages. And it all works out. And they come out to having spent exactly the amounts of time we've calculated—15 years in one case, and 25 years in the other case. This process really does occur, and it's happening to all manifestations of time. The twin's body really ages 15 years in the process of her trip. Your body really ages 25 years. It's not about clocks. It's about time itself and all processes, including aging, that involve time.

Well, I talked in the beginning about time travel. My first lecture was called "Time Travel, Tunneling, Tennis, and Tea." Time travel. In a way, your twin sister, in this experiment, has traveled into the future. She's traveled 10 years into your future. She's now only 15 years older, and you're 25 years older. Could she do better than that? The answer is yes. And to see that, I want to look very quickly, once again, at the time dilation formula that we developed. Again, this is something that, if you've had high school algebra, you could derive yourself. So it's not very mysterious. And it simply says the time as measured in the spaceship's clock is the time as measured in the Earth clock times this factor: $1-v^2$ square rooted. And again, nothing special here about Earth and spaceship. This doesn't happen because you're in space or because you're in a spaceship. It happens because you have one clock moving to be present at two events versus two clocks that are at rest with respect to each other at those separate events.

Look what happens if v gets close to 1. In our units, $v=1$ means the speed of light. That square root gets close to zero. And the square root of zero is zero. So that number, t prime, can be made as small as you want. In the case of the Earth's star trip, if the twin goes faster and faster, she can make the time elapse in her clock, not 15 years, but one year, or one hour, or one second if she goes fast enough. If she goes very fast, she'll be going at almost the speed of light, and the trip will take just a hair over 10 years out, as far as Earth is concerned, and just a hair over 10 years back, for just a hair over 20 years. So, for that Earth-star trip, the minimum time that could take in the Earth-star frame of reference is just over 20 years for speeds that are very close to the speed of light. But she can make that time as short as she wants, as close to zero as she wants by going as close as possible to the speed of light.

Remarkable. In that case, for a trip to a star 10 light years distance, she could come back almost, but not quite, 20 years younger. With the 0.8 speed of light, it was 15 years younger. It could be 20 years younger. She can do better than that though.

Suppose she wanted to go to the Andromeda galaxy. The Andromeda galaxy is the only other galaxy than our own that is just barely visible to the naked eye. It's sort of to the right of the constellation Cassiopeia. On a clear night sky you can see it as a fuzzy little blob. It's 2 million light years away.

So, suppose she goes to the Andromeda, 2 million light years distant. And you might say, she's never going to make it. How can you go 2 million light years when the human life span is only 80 years or something? But she can because she can go as fast as she wants. And she can make t prime as short as she wants. So she can get there in a year, say, or a day, or whatever she wants, going as fast as she wants. If she's going almost the speed of light—the galaxy is 2 million light years away—at the speed of light, that would take 2 million years, judged by somebody in the Earth and galaxy frame of reference, they're essentially at rest with respect to each other.

So, the outgoing trip takes a minimum of 2 million years. Two million years coming back. As far as somebody in Earth is concerned, that trip takes a minimum of 4 million years. But she can make it take as close to zero time as she wants. And so, she'll come back to Earth. And she'll be 4 million years in the future. Her twin brother is long gone. Civilization, as we know it, is probably long gone. She's traveled 4 million years into the future. And how much time has elapsed for her, and her body, and her clocks and her spaceship, and all those things? An hour? A day? Twenty-five years? Whatever it was, depending on how close that v is to the speed of light. How close the v is to 1 in our equation.

Remarkable. She can travel into the future. There's a problem. If she gets there and doesn't like what she finds, maybe Earth is gone, maybe civilization has made a runaway greenhouse effect, like on Venus, and the planet is no longer habitable—all kinds of things could happen. If she doesn't like it, there's no going back. She can't get back to her time. She can leap frog further into the future with another trip. In fact, she could get even further into the future, she could get 2 billion years into the future by going to a galaxy a billion light years away at such a high speed that her time is negligible. Remarkable. Time travel, into the future, is possible. But you can't go back.

Well, this sounds absurd. Does it really happen? It has happened, and it's been demonstrated in an experiment, which I list, incidentally, in the bibliography for this course. Some articles in *Science* magazine from a couple of decades ago took very sensitive atomic clocks, put them in airplanes, and flew them around the Earth. One clock was left behind. Other clocks went around in the aircraft. They went in a circular path—that's nonuniform motion. They came back. The two clocks were compared and they differed, in that case, by about 300 nanoseconds—300 billionths of a second. Not a big amount of time but easily measurable by today's standards.

In that experiment we had the effects of special relativity. We also had some effects from general relativity, because of changes in gravity with the airplane's altitude. And we'll get to those later. But the fact is, those experiments confirm, remarkably, although with fairly trivial change in time, the time dilation formula. The twin event really does occur. The traveling clock really did come back younger—in that case by only 300 billionths of a second. But it did come back younger. Time travel to the future really can occur, and it really is possible.

Lecture Ten
Escaping Contradiction: Simultaneity is Relative

Scope:

There seems to be a big problem with time dilation: "Moving clocks run slow," but who's to say which clock is moving? If clock B sees clock A move by and concludes that clock A is "running slow," why can't clock A claim to see clock B go by and conclude that B is "running slow"? It can! There's no contradiction, because of another remarkable implication of the principle of relativity: Two events that are simultaneous (i.e., that occur at the same time) in one frame of reference are not simultaneous in another frame moving relative to the first. It is this relativity of simultaneity that allows two observers in relative motion to see each other's clocks "run slow," without contradiction.

Why is it that simultaneity is relative? Another look at the star trip shows that the distance between Earth and the star must be less than 10 light-years as measured in the spaceship's frame of reference. Length, like time, is also relative. An object is longest in a frame in which it is at rest and shorter in frames in which it is moving—by the same relativistic factor that arises in time dilation. Consider two high-speed airplanes moving in opposite directions. In a frame in which they are moving with the same speed, they have the same length. Their left ends coincide at the same time as their right ends. In any other frame, they have different lengths, so the left ends don't coincide at the same time as the right ends. The events of the two respective ends coinciding are not simultaneous and even occur in different time order in different frames. But doesn't this violate causality? No, because only those events that can't be causally related can have different time ordering for different observers.

Outline

I. Problem: "Moving clocks run slow," but relativity precludes either of two clocks in relative motion from asserting absolutely "I am moving; you're not." Each can say the other "runs slow."So how is time dilation not a contradiction?

A. Recall that we arrived at time dilation by considering *one* clock that moves past *two* others that are at rest relative to each other and that are *synchronized*—meaning the events of their hands pointing to a given time are simultaneous.

1. Those events are simultaneous in the clocks' own frame.

2. Remarkably, as we'll see shortly, relativity implies that events simultaneous in one frame of reference are not simultaneous in another frame.

3. They are not simultaneous in the frame of the "moving" clock. In fact, the right-hand clock reads a later time, and that is why the elapsed time on the two clocks is longer than on the "moving" clock, even though the "moving" clock judges the other two to be "running slow." There is no contradiction; observers in each frame judge the other's clocks to be "running slow," and each is correct.

B. In general, the relativity of simultaneity explains many of the apparent paradoxes that arise in relativity. They are only paradoxical if one insists that simultaneity is an absolute concept—and it isn't.

II. Why simultaneity is relative (or why events that are simultaneous in one frame of reference are not simultaneous in another   frame of reference).

A. Revisiting the star trip reveals the phenomenon of *length contraction*.

1. Earth–star distance was 10 light-years in Earth–star frame. But the spaceship made the trip in 7.5 years, going at $0.8c$. Therefore, in the ship frame, the distance must have been (0.8 ly/y) $\square$ (7.5 years) = 6 light-years.

2. In general, the length of an object is longest in a frame in which the object is at rest. (Here, the "object" is the Earth–star system, 10 light-years long to an observer at rest in that frame.) An object is shorter when measured in a frame of reference in which it is moving, with the contraction given by the same factor $\sqrt{1 - v^2}$ that arises in time dilation.

3. This is called "Lorentz contraction" (or sometimes "Fitzgerald contraction"). Recall from Lecture Six that they came up with the right idea for the wrong reason.

4. An example in which length contraction is important is the Stanford Linear Accelerator, which is 2 miles long as measured on Earth, but only about 3 feet long to the electrons moving down the accelerator at $0.9999995c$. Even a TV picture tube, in which electrons attain about $0.3c$, would not focus correctly if engineers did not take length contraction into account.

5. Being relativistically correct: Isn't the distance between Earth and star "really" 10 light-years and the length of the Stanford Linear Accelerator "really" 2 miles? No! To claim so is to give special status to one frame of reference, and that is precisely what relativity precludes. Be careful of using the word "really" when talking about relativity.

B. Relativity of simultaneity: Consider two high-speed airplanes (very high speed!) passing each other in opposite directions.

1. There is some frame of reference in which both have the same speed and, therefore, the same length (although it is shorter than their "rest length"). In this frame, the left ends of the two planes coincide at the same time that the right ends coincide; the events of the two ends coinciding are, therefore, simultaneous.

2. In a frame in which the upper airplane is at rest, the right ends of the two planes coincide before the left ends, so the events aren't simultaneous.

3. In a frame in which the lower airplane is at rest, the time order of the two events is reversed.

4. Continuing this line of reasoning, would it be possible for your birth and death to occur at the same time?

C. Is there a problem with causality? After all, if the time order of events can be reversed in different reference frames, there might be. But there is no problem; we'll see why in the next lecture.

Essential Reading:

Mook and Vargish, *Inside Relativity*, Chapter 4, pp. 111–113.

Suggested Reading:

Moore, *A Traveler's Guide to Spacetime*, Chapter 3.

Questions to Consider:

1. Devise an experiment that observers in the reference frame of clock A could do to verify that, as measured in the upper clock's frame, both the clocks in the lower frame are "running slow."

2. A famous "paradox" of relativity is the following: A high-speed runner carries a 10-foot-long pole toward a barn that is 10 feet long and has doors open at both ends. The runner is going so fast that, from the point of view of the farmer who owns the barn, the pole is only 5 feet long. Clearly, the farmer can close both barn doors and trap the runner in the barn. But to the runner, the pole is 10 feet long and the barn, rushing toward the runner, is only 5 feet long. So clearly the runner can't be in the barn with both doors closed. Can you resolve the paradox, using the fact that events simultaneous in one reference frame aren't simultaneous in another? (By the way, the speed required here is $0.866c$.)

Who's Moving? Who's "Running Slow"?

A: I'm at rest,
B is moving
so B "runs slow"

A

Who's right ?

B

Both !

B: I'm at rest,
A is moving
so A "runs slow"

This diagram illustrates what initially seems to be a contradiction created by the Principle of Relativity. Because the laws of physics are valid in all frames of reference in uniform motion, observers in the reference frame of each clock can draw the same conclusions about the other clock. Thus the following statements hold:

#1. From a frame of reference in which Clock A is at rest, Clock B is in motion and thus is "running slow" compared to Clock A.
#2. From a frame of reference in which clock B is at rest, Clock A is in motion and thus is "running slow" compared to Clock B.

The two statements seem to be completely contradictory, but relativity insists that both are correct. The explanation lies in the fact that simultaneity itself is actually relative, as can be seen in Dr. Wolfson's later arguments.

The Situation in Different Frames of Reference

This diagram illustrates the same experiment, viewed from two separate frames of reference. In the experiment, clock A moves from clock B_1 to clock B_2, similar to the experiment in Lecture 8.

Box One details the experiment as seen from the frame of reference of clocks B_1 and B_2. In this frame, the two clocks are synchronized and an observer in the B-clock frame can conclude that clock A "runs slow" as it moves between B_1 and B_2.
Box Two details the exact same experiment from the frame of reference of Clock A.
To observers in this frame, the B clocks are running slow.

The problem of contradiction is resolved through the concept of relative simultaneity. While the B clocks are synchronized in *their* frame of reference, they are *not* synchronized in A's frame of reference. Although they're "running slow," clock B_2 is ahead and thus the elapsed time $(B_2 - B_1)$ is still longer than that measured on clock A.

The Situation in B's Frame of Reference

Box One

B_1 and B_2 are synchronized.

A

B_2

B_1

The Situation in A's Frame of Reference

Box Two

A

B_1 and B_2 are not synchronized.

B_1

B_2

Star Trip, Revisited

In spaceship's frame of reference:

Earth-star trip takes 7.5 years at $0.8c$

Therefore distance is:

distance = speed × time

= $(0.8 \text{ ly/y}) \times (7.5 \text{ years})$

= 6 light-years

0.8c

6 light-years

Two Identical Airplanes Pass

In a frame where both are moving, their ends coincide at the same time:

In a frame where the upper plane is at rest, their right ends coincide first:

In a frame where the lower plane is at rest, their left ends coincide first:

181

Lecture Ten—Transcript
Escaping Contradiction: Simultaneity is Relative

Welcome to Lecture Ten. The first part of my title for Lecture Ten is "Escaping Contradiction." People who study relativity at first seem to be stuck with the idea that there are an awful lot of contradictions here. There seem to be a lot of things that could not really be true. How can we possibly have time dilation? How can we possibly have the twin being younger? And, yet, the other twin isn't younger. And these seem to be contradictions.

Most of the contradictions are resolved by a fact that's spelled out in the second half of my title, namely, that simultaneity is relative. What it means to say that two events are simultaneous—occur at the same time—actually depends on your frame of reference. And we're going to explore that in some detail in this lecture.

This is about the most technical look we're going to have at special relativity. Not mathematical. But we're getting pretty much into the thick of it and drawing conclusions thick and fast from, ultimately, the principle of relativity. If you're feeling a little bit lost at this point, you might want to hit rewind and go back to the last couple of lectures and convince yourself that you see how all this must follow from nothing more than the principle of relativity—that the laws of physics are the same for all observers in uniform motion. There is nothing else coming in here. There is nothing new. Nothing beyond that.

We're just exploring the implications of that one simple fact. And I'd like to look at a seeming contradiction that may, or may not, have occurred to you yet but is implicit in our discussion of time dilation, and that rather poor phrasing of it by the phrase "moving clocks run slow." What's wrong with that phrase, of course, and I asked you to think about this at one point, what's wrong with that phrase is neither clock has the right to say the other is moving and I'm at rest. Each frame of reference is an equally good frame of reference for doing physics. Each is entitled to say, "Oh, I'm here and you're moving relative to me." The other frame can say, "Yeah, well, but you're moving relative to me." And they're both right.

And I want to explore the implications of that briefly for this statement that "moving clocks run slow." And I think I'll show you in the process why that's such a bad phrase to use in describing time dilation.

Here is your clock. You're at rest, with respect to that clock, and I'm going to go by you with my clock. I'm moving, relative to you. And if you wanted to set up one of those time dilation experiments, you would say, "Oh, Wolfson's clock is the moving the clock, mine's the clock at rest. His clock runs slow."

Now the way you would set that experiment up, remember, is to have a second clock and compare the time when my clock passes your first clock and the second clock, and so on. But the essence of the statement you would arrive at is, "Oh, Wolfson's clock is running slow, because he is moving relative to me." Now, naively, you might think, well, if my clock is moving slow compared to yours, yours must be moving fast compared to mine. But that violates the spirit of relativity, because the spirit of relativity says no frame of reference is special. My frame of reference is just as good a frame of reference for doing physics as is your frame of reference. Provided, at least, I'm moving uniformly.

Remember, it was that non-uniformity of the twin's motion when she turned around at the distant star that broke that symmetry. But at this point I'm simply going to be moving past you in uniform motion, and my frame of reference is just as good a frame of reference as yours on Earth. Nothing special about Earth or Earth's state of motion. I'm in just as good a frame of reference as you are for doing physics. And therefore, I should draw exactly the same conclusions you do, in exactly the same situation.

So what conclusions do I draw? Well, I'm at rest in my frame of reference. And I see your clock going by me. Your clock's moving relative to me. And therefore, your clock must run slow. And if I wanted to set this up very carefully, I would take a second clock in my frame of reference, and I would watch the time when my first clock passed yours, and my second, and so on. And I'd do the time dilation experiment, exactly as we did it in the preceding two lectures. And I would come to exactly the same conclusion that your clock moves slow compared to mine. Runs slow compared to mine.

How can that possibly be? There's one of the seeming contradictions of relativity. Two clocks are in relative motion. Each one must conclude that the other runs slow. If that weren't the case, then we would have an asymmetric situation, and one of them would be able to say, oh, that one's moving fast and this one's moving slower. That one's at rest, and this one isn't at rest. And that's exactly what relativity precludes us from doing, because relativity says all the laws of physics, all the conclusions you draw from the laws of physics, are the same in all uniformly moving frames of reference.

How can that be though? Well, the resolution lies, as I said, in the second half of my title, "Simultaneity is Relative." And we'll come to that in a minute. But before we do, let's look in a little bit more detail about exactly how we do this time dilation measurement. Here we've got two clocks—clock A and clock B. And we're raising the question, who's moving? And who's running slow? Here's what clock B thinks. Clock B says, "I'm at rest, A is moving, so A runs slow." But A says, "No, I'm at rest, B is moving, so B runs slow." That's exactly the situation I just demonstrated for you. So which one of these clocks is right?

Well, the answer is both are right. How are we going to resolve this? How are we going to understand that this is not a contradiction? Well, let's look at the situation in the reference frame of clock B and how clock B would really set up an experiment to prove, or show, that clock A is "running slow."

Here's how clock B would do it. It would do exactly what we've done in the previous couple of lectures. We would have a couple of clocks in some frame of reference. That's clock B's frame of reference. Those clocks are at rest with respect to each other. And clock A is going to move relative to that frame of reference in such a way that it goes from clock B-1 to clock B-2. And we're going to compare the elapsed time on clock A with the time that elapses on clocks B-1 and B-2. And we already know the answer. The time elapsed in clock A is going to be shorter by that square rootish factor. That doesn't matter. It's going to be shorter. That's the important point. That's the situation in B's frame of reference.

Now we have to look at one other thing that I didn't mention before when we set this experiment up. B has two clocks. And in order for this experiment to have any meaning, in order for the time interval measured on those two clocks to make sense, B has got to make sure those clocks are synchronized. That is, they both point to 12 noon or 10 o'clock, as they're shown in the picture, at exactly the same time. Otherwise, they're not keeping time right. I mean, they may be running at the same rate, but unless they're also synchronized—they point to the same time at the same instant—we've got a problem. And we won't be able to do the measurement carefully or accurately, because one of the clocks won't have been set right. No problem. You know, you start some operation and say "synchronized watches, folks." Well, everybody's watch has got to read the same thing if we're going to be talking about the same time.

The same is true here. To do this experiment, clock B-1 and clock B-2 have to be synchronized. They have to be running at the same rate. Well, they are, because they're perfect clocks and they're in the same frame of reference. That's no problem. But they also have to be set to the same time at the same instant. And I didn't stress that before, because it was so obvious. But, in fact, it's not quite so obvious. It's a bit subtle. And now I want to stress it. And I want to raise the question, how, in fact, would one synchronize those clocks, because they are, after all, located at different places. One thing we know we cannot do is bring them together. Set them, you know, something like this. Bring them together, set them until they read exactly the same, and then run this one over here. Because if I do that, this clock has spent some time in a different frame of reference. And then it's keeping time at a different rate. And then they have failed to be synchronized. That will not work.

There are ways to synchronize the two clocks, though. For example, if I know how far apart they are. Let's say they're one light year apart. Pretty far, but it's a good example. Let's say they're one light year apart. Or make it one light hour apart, that'll be easier. Make them one light hour apart. Okay, what do I do? At noon, I set clock B-1 to noon, and at the same instant I send out a light flash, and I say, hey, B-2, when you get that light flash, set yourself to—what should it be? Not noon, but one o'clock, because we know it's taken one hour for the light flash to go one light hour. That will assure that those clocks are synchronized.

But notice it's a little bit subtle because the way I can communicate between the two clocks, the fastest way I know how is by sending a light signal, or a radio wave, or some other electromagnetic wave. And that takes time because that wave travels at speed c. I cannot simply bring the clocks together and then separate them because then one of them at least has to go in a different frame of reference.

There's a more symmetrical way of synchronizing. If I'd like, I could go into the position in my frame of reference that's midway between the two clocks. And I could send out a flash of light. And I could say, okay folks, when you get this flash of light, both of you set yourself to time zero, or some specified time, whatever it is. And whether or not we get the absolute time right, in that frame of reference, we at least will have the two clocks saying the same time at the same instant, if, in fact, we send out this light flash from a point midway in between them. So, it is possible to synchronize two clocks that are at rest with respect to each other in a frame of reference. But it is a little bit subtle. But it's entirely possible to do. But we do have to take in to account the finite speed of light.

So, we assume we've achieved that synchronization, and we've achieved it in this frame of reference. So here's the situation. Clocks B-1 and B-2 are synchronized. And again, that was so obvious I didn't even mention it before. But now it's crucial to an understanding of what's going on.

Back to the second half of my title. First half—"Escaping Contradiction." Here we have this seeming contradiction. Clock A says clock B is running slow. Clock B says clock A is running slow. How can it be true for both of them? I asserted it had to be true for both of them. It is true for both of them. How is it not a contradiction? "Escaping Contradiction, Simultaneity is Relative." Let me say that in great big letters. Events that are simultaneous in one frame of reference are not simultaneous in another frame of reference. Two events that occur at the same time in one frame of reference, do not, cannot occur at the same time in another frame of reference. I'm going to ask you to accept that statement for the next five or ten minutes, but then I'm going to prove it to you before the end of this lecture. I'm going to show you why that has to be. Events that are simultaneous in one frame of reference are not simultaneous in another frame of reference.

There is an exception to that I just ought to mention in case you get picky about this. The exception is two events that occur at exactly the same place and the same time—those two events can be simultaneous. But they're really, essentially, the same event then. If two events happen, if I snap this finger and snap this finger at the same time and the same place—literally the same place—those two events are simultaneous by anyone who cares to observe it, because they take place right at the same place. But the minute they're separated in space—I snap my fingers simultaneously—there are observers for whom those events are not simultaneous. There are observers for whom this snapping occurs before this one. And there are observers for whom this snapping occurs before this one. And you say to yourself, "Yeah, but you really snapped them at the same time." And if you say that, you're saying Wolfson's frame of reference is special. It's the only frame of reference where things are really true. I don't believe in relativity. I can throw this whole course out the window, because I don't accept the principle of relativity. If you say, they're really simultaneous in my frame, you're singling out a special frame of reference in which the laws of physics are right and they aren't right in all the other frames. And that simply isn't what relativity is about.

What relativity is about is the statement that the laws of physics are the same in all uniformly moving frames of reference. So if there is another uniformly moving frame of reference in which these two events are not simultaneous, then that is just as legitimate a picture of reality. And indeed, in that frame of reference the events are not simultaneous and there is no "really" about it. To me they are simultaneous; to an observer in another frame of reference they're not.

We'll see why that is by the end of the lecture. But let's see what that does to the problem, the contradiction, we seem to have with the time dilation situation in which clock B says, "Oh, clock A is moving relative to me. It's running slower." Clock A says, "Oh, clock B is moving relative to me. It's running slower." And I say they're both right. They are both right. Here's how.

We're going to look at the situation next in clock A's frame of reference. We've been looking all the while in clock B's frame. We've been drawing the picture of the two clocks in B's frame of reference and the one clock moving between them. Let's now look at the situation in clock A's frame of reference. And remember, events that are simultaneous in one frame of reference are not simultaneous in another. I'm going to prove that to you. Hold on to that for just a little bit.

What are the simultaneous events we're talking about in this case? Well, the simultaneous events were the setting of the two clocks. In B's frame of reference, clock B-1 and B-2 were set to the same time at the same instant. In my picture, they were both set to read 10 o'clock at the same instant. How? Well, there was this synchronizing process. B-1 sent out a light signal, and B-2 set itself to the time B-1 told it—the time B-1 was reading when it sent out the light signal plus the time it took the light signal to travel. And then they were synchronized. Or we put somebody midway in between them, and they sent out a light flash in both directions. And the two clocks set themselves to the same time when they received the light flash. And then they were synchronized. So, they've been synchronized in B's frame of reference, in the frame of reference in which those two clocks are at rest.

But clock A is moving past, from B-1 toward B-2, relative to that frame of reference. And I just told you—again not yet with proof, but I will prove it soon—I've just told you that events that are simultaneous in one frame of reference cannot be simultaneous in another frame of reference. May I take that back a little bit—in another frame of reference moving on a line between the two events. They can't be simultaneous. If it were moving sideways, might be. Events that are simultaneous in one frame of reference are not simultaneous in another frame of reference.

Well, here we have clock A moving on a line between clocks B-1 and B-2. The events of setting the two clocks in B's frame to, say, 10 o'clock—which is what they show in the picture—those events are simultaneous in B's frame of reference. Therefore, they cannot be simultaneous in A's frame of reference. Therefore, from A's point of view, the two clocks do not read 10 o'clock at the same time. That's what it means to say the events are not simultaneous. What are the events? The events are the events of the two clocks reading 10 o'clock. Those events are simultaneous in B's frame. We set the two clocks together to 10 o'clock. They, therefore, cannot be simultaneous in A's frame. Therefore, as far as A is concerned, the two clocks cannot point to 10 o'clock at the same instant.

And so, what does the situation look like in A's frame of reference? Here's the situation in A's frame of reference. It sees clock B-1 and clock B-2 going past it to the left. Why to the left? Because in B's frame of reference, we had clock A moving past to the right. So, clock A sees clock B-1 and B-2 moving to the left. And I haven't, again, proved rigorously why it happens this particular direction. But, in fact, it's the case that clock B-2, in the set up of this situation in which B-1 and B-2 are moving past A to the left, and B-2 is further to the right, B-2 will be reading a later time at the instant that B-1 reads 10 o'clock. So, that's the situation from A's point of view.

Now, remember what occurred in this whole time dilation thing. The elapsed time on A was shorter than on B-1 and B-2, as measured for the event of A passing B-1 and then A passing B-2. From A's point of view, it's B-1 passes A and then B-2 passes A. A measures an elapsed time, which is short. A says, "Wait a minute, clocks B-1 and B-2 should be running slow. So they should measure a shorter elapsed time." Well, they sort of do. But the problem is clock B-2 is ahead. And so even though clocks B-1 and B-2 are "running slower," as far as A is concerned—because it's completely reciprocal—because clock B-2 is ahead, when A compares the time on clock B-1 and the time on clock B-2, and when they pass, it will see that clock B-2 is further advanced. Why? Because B-2 is already ahead of the game. So what if it's running slower, it's already ahead in time, because the events of the two clocks reading 10 o'clock were not simultaneous.

So there's the key to that contradiction. It is really true that clock B, the B clocks, say clock A is running slow. It's also true that clock A says the B clocks are running slow. Everybody agrees that the difference in time between clock B-2 and clock B-1, for the events of the clock A passing B-1 and then B-2, everybody agrees that that interval is longer than the interval elapsed on clock A between those two events. Everyone agrees. But the interpretation is different. The interpretation in B's case is, "Oh, A is running slower. So, of course, less time elapses."

The interpretation A is a little more complicated. A says, "Well, the clocks in B are running slow. If they were synchronized, then less time would elapse in B. But they're not synchronized. Clock B-2, the right-most clock, is further ahead. So the elapsed time I get by subtracting the measurement in B-1 from the measurement in B-2 is still longer than the time on clock A. Even though those clocks are running slow." Now, A's interpretation is, those clocks were not synchronized. That's a bit to think about.

You might want to go back and review that a few times. But there is the way out of the contradiction. It really is true that if a clock goes by me and I say, quote, it's running slow, it can say my clocks are running slow, and there is no contradiction. And the lack of contradiction comes about because events that are simultaneous in one frame of reference are not simultaneous in another. Well, why is that?

Let's revisit that star trip we took in the last lecture. Here's the star trip. We had a trip of what seemed to be 10 light years distance. We were going at $0.8c$. I'm going to assert now, that that trip is not 10 light years distance as measured in the spaceship's frame of reference. And we can easily see why that is. The spaceship, after all, is moving at $0.8c$, and it goes some distance, which we thought was 10 light years. But I'm going to show you it isn't 10 light years now. It's going at $0.8c$, 0.8 light years per year. We know that it takes 7.5 years. We figured that out. So distance equals speed times time, which is 0.8 of a light year per year times 7.5 years, and that comes out six light years. It must be the case with the distance between the Earth and star, in the ship's frame of reference, is not 10 light years, but six light years. It would be a contradiction if that weren't true. Distance equals speed times time wouldn't be true. It is true. And the answer is that the distance is different. The spatial interval is different.

That shouldn't surprise you. We've already seen that temporal intervals—the interval between two events in time—is different in different frames of reference. Now, I'm telling you the interval between two events in space, the interval between the event of the ship passing Earth and the event of the ship passing the star is different in a different frame of reference. And, in this case, the difference is given by the original distance in the frame in which the two objects were at rest, multiplied by that factor, $1-v^2$.

So if I take this meter stick, this is true of any object, if I take this meter stick and I move it along in my frame of reference, it's a perfectly good meter stick. It's a meter long. But if you measure it, and I'm coming toward you, say, at $0.8c$, you'll measure this meter stick to be 60 centimeters long. There's that square root of $1-0.8^2$ factor coming in again. It's really a meter long. Well, you can try to say that. But if you say that, you're saying the frame of reference where it's at rest is the special frame. In a way, that's a special frame for the meter stick. But, if somebody else is in another frame of reference and they measure it and they get 60 centimeters, 0.6 meters, they're right, too.

Measures of space are not absolute any more than measures of time are. Not a surprise. Space and time are the things we had to give up the absoluteness of when we accepted the absoluteness of the laws of physics. The fact that the laws of physics are the same for all observers in uniform motion. We gave up space and time being absolute when we first did that first experiment where I handed you a clock and a meter stick, and I put you in a car or an airplane or a spaceship, and we determined that you measured the same speed for light that I did. How could that be? Well, I said, "Well, something strange must have happened to your meter stick or your clock or maybe both. So that despite the fact that you're moving relative to me, you get the same answer for the speed of light that I did."

Well, something, "strange" has happened to both clock and meter stick, because something strange has happened to time and space. But be careful. That "strange" word is another dangerous, loaded, nonrelativistically correct one. Things are perfectly normal in your frame of reference. That's a meter stick. It measures a meter long. That's a perfect clock. And it keeps perfect time. It's just the time it's measuring, and the space the meter stick is measuring, are not the same quantities that my stick and my clock are measuring. They're different quantities. We'll see later on that they are, in fact, aspects of a more unified, four-dimensional quantity, which we all agree on, that has to do with spacetime. We'll get to that soon.

But in fact, measures of space and time are no longer absolute in relativity. And we simply don't notice the fact that measures of space and time are relative to the observer, because we don't have a lot of observers whizzing around at speeds that are a substantial fraction of the speed of light. But in fact that's the case. Measures of space and time are not absolute. And we now know how to find them out in these simple cases, in cases like the time dilation experiment we know the time on the clock moving from here to here, versus the two clocks that are at rest with respect to each other, is smaller by that factor of the square root of $1-v^2$. And, similarly, the distance between two events is smaller by that factor of $1-v^2$ in this particular kind of example.

So, I've convinced you now of something called *length contraction*. The length of an object—if you want to be really precise about it, the spatial interval between events of the one end of the object passing and another end of the object passing, and so on, if we want to be really rigorous about it—but let's just say the length of an object is greatest in a frame of reference where the object is at rest. When I'm at rest, with respect to this meter stick, it's one meter long. When I move it, like this, it's still one meter long, with respect to me. But it's shorter with respect to you by that factor, square root of one minus velocity, when the velocity is measured in terms of speed of light squared. That's called length contraction. It's also called the Lorentz contraction, again, after that Dutch physicist Lorentz—or the Lorentz-Fitzgerald contraction after the Dutch physicist Lorentz and his Irish colleague, Fitzgerald, who, as I described after the Michelson-Morley experiment, came up with the idea that maybe objects compress in the direction of motion due to their motion through the ether. They came up with the right formula. They came up with this phenomenon. They just had no basis for it whatsoever. They thought there really was a real length and the ether somehow compressed things. Well, things do compress in the direction of motion, but it's not because some physical effect of the moving squeezes them together. Don't look for that any more than you look for something tugging back the hands of the clock to slow down the clock. These are effects that are happening to space and time themselves. Not to the objects that are in space and time.

The meter stick is shorter because space itself is different in that frame of reference, not because the meter stick has somehow squished with respect to some absolute space. So don't get yourself talking nonrelativistically, don't say, it "really" is such. Don't look for the atoms to move a little closer together or something. All measures of space are contracted in that different frame of reference relative to what they were in another frame of reference. But neither frame is justified in saying, I'm the right one.

How does this lead to nonsimultaneity? How does it lead to the relativity of simultaneity? Well, that's actually quite easy to see once you accept the fact that length contraction occurs. Let me give you a couple of examples where length contraction is important though before we go on. It doesn't bother us in everyday life, again, because we don't move at speeds that are near that of the speed of light.

But there are a number of situations, in high-energy physics particularly, where we worry about it a lot. Remember those muons that were coming down Mount Washington. Mount Washington is 6,000 feet high. Not to those muons. The muons see Mount

Washington length-contracted; it's only 700 feet high. That's why they last so long. They're only going 700 feet. Time dilation, length contraction, they're aspects of the same thing. The different measures of space and time in different frames of reference.

If you've ever been to Stanford University, driving down Interstate 280 in California, you cross a very, very long concrete structure. It's two miles long. You cross it just south of the northern-most exit to Stanford University. It's the Stanford linear accelerator. It's two miles long. It's a giant particle accelerator that accelerates subatomic particles to speeds almost that of light.

Electrons get up to 0.9999995 the speed of light in that thing. In the electron's frame of reference, the Stanford linear accelerator—two miles long in the Earth's reference frame—is only three feet long. Isn't it really two miles long? No. Because the electron's frame of reference is just as good as yours for doing physics, and for asserting the reality of physical entities, and for doing physical measurements and stating the results. It's really three feet long to those electrons. And if the engineers who designed it didn't take that in to account, it wouldn't work at all.

Similarly, your TV tube is shorter by a factor of the square root of $1-0.3^2$, which isn't a big factor but is measurable to the electrons barreling down it to paint the picture than it is to you and me sitting here in the room where the TV tube is. And if the engineers who designed that tube didn't take that into account, the picture would not be in focus. So, there are cases where length contraction is an important phenomenon. And there are cases where objects are moving at speeds approximately that of light, or close to that of light.

Okay, let's go on now and use this fact of length contraction to look at why events that are simultaneous in one frame of reference can't be simultaneous in another frame of reference. Okay, I'm going to imagine a situation in which two identical airplanes pass each other. And I'm going to draw this situation in three different reference frames. One, in a reference frame where both are moving. So, these two airplanes are going to be coming at each other from opposite directions. In this frame of reference, they're going to pass each other. I'm sitting in this frame of reference. The two airplanes are moving with respect to me. They're moving at the same speed, but in opposite directions. And so they're already going to be length-contracted. So, here are the two airplanes coming at each other. And

I've drawn them a certain length. And that is their contracted length. That's not the length they would have if I were at rest with respect to them. That's a shorter length.

And I'm going to ask the question about two events. And the events are the coinciding of the tail of the upper airplane and the nose of the lower airplane. And the nose of the upper airplane and the tail of the lower airplane. Those are the two events I'm concerned about. And again, this goes far beyond airplanes. This is about any two events as judged in different frames of reference. In this frame of reference, the two airplanes are the same length, because in this frame of reference they're moving at the same speed. And although they're length-contracted, they're length-contracted by the same amount.

So, what happens when they get opposite each other? Well, you can see that the tail of the upper airplane and the nose of the right airplane are side by side at the same instant that the nose of the upper airplane and the tail of the lower airplane are side by side. The two events, of the tails and noses coinciding, are simultaneous events in this frame of reference, in the frame of reference where the two airplanes are moving at the same speed.

Now, let's look at that in a different frame of reference. Here's going to be a frame of reference where the upper plane is going to be at rest, and the lower plane is going to be moving—therefore, faster than it was in the frame of reference where both were moving. So, what's it look like? We have a great big airplane—long. That's its rest length. That's a length in a frame of reference at rest with respect to us. And the lower airplane is foreshortened even more. And it's moving very fast, whereas the upper airplane, in this frame of reference, is at rest.

What happens? Well, the first of the two events we were worried about is the nose of the upper airplane coincides with the tail of the lower airplane. Obvious. But at the same instant, the tail of the upper airplane and nose of the lower airplane are not coinciding. In fact, it's a while later that that second event occurs. The two events that were simultaneous in the first frame of reference—the frame in which the two airplanes were moving toward each other at the same speed—those events are not simultaneous in this other frame of reference.

And we can go to yet another frame of reference. We can go to a frame of reference in which the lower airplane is at rest. And what's going to happen there? The lower airplane is at rest. It's now its normal "rest length." The length it has in a frame of reference at rest with respect to it. The upper one is foreshortened. Just like the lower one was last time. And what event is first? It's the event of the tail of the upper plane coinciding with the nose of the lower plane. And a while later, the next event—that occurred first in the previous frame of reference—now occurs later. So, events that are simultaneous in the first frame of reference are not simultaneous in the other two frames of reference.

And it's even worse than that. Their time order is, in fact, reversed. In one case, this event occurs later. In the other case, this event occurred first. Not only are the events not simultaneous, but their time order is even relative. Whoa. Does that mean your death could occur before your birth in some frame of reference? Fortunately, it doesn't. There is only a certain class of events for which the reversal of order is possible. They're events that can be simultaneous, in some frame of reference. Not all can. There is no frame of reference in which your birth and death are simultaneous. I guarantee you. And we'll see why soon. In fact, we'll see why in the next lecture. We're going to explore the question of causality. Is it possible for events to have their time order reversed without throwing out the window the whole concept of cause and effect, because we usually think cause occurs before effect. And if the time order can reverse, what's happened to causality? We'll see that in the next lecture.

Lecture Eleven

Faster than Light? Past, Future, and Elsewhere

Scope:

That the time order of events can be different in different reference frames seems to wreak havoc with cause and effect. Is there some frame in which your death precedes your birth, for example? No, the only events for which the time order can be different are those that occur far enough apart in space that it would be impossible for a light signal to get from one event to the other. Because no information can travel faster than light (more on this soon), such events cannot influence each other and can be neither cause nor effect of the other. Those events define a new realm of time, called the *elsewhere*.

Why can't anything go faster than light? The simplest answer follows directly from the principle of relativity: Because any observer must always measure the value c for the speed of light, you can never find yourself at rest with respect to light. Because light goes at speed c relative to all observers, that means you can't go at c relative to any observer. Furthermore, the fact that measures of space and time differ for different observers prevents you from "leapfrogging" past c by moving rapidly with respect to a reference frame that itself is moving rapidly relative to yet another frame.

Outline

I. Relativity and causality.

    A. Time between any two events depends on the frame of reference from which the events are measured (as time dilation examples show). To clarify, an *event* is specified by giving both a place and a time.

    B. However, the *time order* of events can differ in different reference frames only if the events are far enough apart in space that not even light travels fast enough to get from one event to another. Because nothing can travel faster than light (more on this shortly), the two events cannot be causally related. Thus, there is no problem with causality. For example, when the Mars Rover was active in the late 1990s, Earth and Mars were 11 light-minutes apart. An event on Earth and one occurring 5 minutes later (Earth–Mars time) on Mars cannot be causally related—and there can be observers for whom the Mars event occurs first. (But doesn't the Earth event *really* occur first? That question is not RC! Think about why not.) Such causally unrelated events define a new realm of time, in addition to past, present, and future.

1. In relativity, the past consists of those events that can influence the present. For example, your birth is in part the cause of your now watching or listening to these lectures. It is in your past, and all observers will agree that it came before your present moment (although they will disagree about the amount of time between your birth and now). But an event simultaneous with your birth (simultaneous in Earth's frame of reference) at the center of our galaxy, 30,000 light-years away, is not in the past because it can't yet affect us.

2. Similarly, the future consists of events that the present can influence. Events that will happen tomorrow on Earth are in the future, and all observers will agree that events on Earth today come before those on Earth tomorrow. However, events that will happen tomorrow at the galactic center are not in the future of the present moment on Earth, because there is no way we can influence them.

3. Those events that are neither in the past nor the future are in the *elsewhere*. They can have no causal relation to the event here and now, and different observers will judge differently whether they occur before, after, or are simultaneous with the here and now. The elsewhere is not some mysterious realm, forever inaccessible; it's just inaccessible to the here and now. Events that are now in your elsewhere will sometime later be in your past and, at some earlier time, they were in your future. But there's a band of time centered on the present—22 minutes for Mars, 60,000 years for the galactic center, 4 million years for Andromeda—during which events are unrelated to the here and now.

4. Again, this gives us a new realm of time to go with our categories of past, present, and future.

II. All this depends on nothing being able to go faster than light. But why is it impossible to go faster than light?

A. It follows from the principle of relativity that light goes at speed c relative to any uniformly moving reference frame. Therefore, there cannot be an observer who is at rest with respect to light. Because you would need to reach the speed of light to go faster still and because you can't be at rest with respect to light, then you can't go faster.

1. More technically, a light wave at rest is simply not a solution to Maxwell's equations of electromagnetism; only a light wave moving at c is. Accepting the principle of relativity—that all of physics, including Maxwell's equations—is valid in all reference frames, then it is impossible to be at rest relative to light and, therefore, impossible to go at speed c. (This is the point Einstein puzzled about at age 16.)

2. Attempting to travel faster than light by "leapfrogging" from one rapidly moving reference frame to another fails, because measures of time and space differ in different reference frames.

3. A more precise statement about faster-than-light travel is that no *information* can be transmitted at speeds faster than light.

4. Is this something special about light? No, it's about *time*; light only provides the extreme case. If a police car going 50 mph clocks you going 30 mph relative to the police car, are you going 80 mph relative to the road? Not quite! The difference is tiny, but it is there and it results from the fact that measures of time and space are different in the different reference frames. As speeds approach c, the effects of this *relativistic velocity addition* become more dramatic and prevent any material objects ever moving at c relative to each other.

B. An important caveat: It is the speed of light *in vacuum* that is the ultimate speed. Light moves slower through transparent materials, such as glass, water, or even air—and there's no problem with objects moving faster than the speed of light in such materials.

   1. High-energy subatomic particles moving through water, for example, often do exceed the speed of light in water and, when they do, they produce shock waves analogous to the sonic booms from supersonic aircraft.

   2. A more sophisticated description of c is not so much that it's the speed of light but rather that it's a conversion factor between units of space and time. If we really wanted to be relativistically correct, we would measure time and space in the same units and c would have the value 1.

Essential Reading:

Hey and Walters, *Einstein's Mirror*, Chapter 4.

Hoffmann, *Relativity and Its Roots*, Chapter 5, pp. 121–127.

Suggested Reading:

Moore, *A Traveler's Guide to Spacetime*, Chapter 8, Section 4.

Taylor and Wheeler, *Spacetime Physics*, Chapter 6.

Questions to Consider:

1. Right now it's "the present," but is it "the present" everywhere? Explain your answer.

2. Suppose a technological civilization evolved 25,000 years ago on the other side of our Milky Way galaxy, 60,000 light-years from Earth. Could there be observers for whom technological civilization emerged first on Earth? What if the extraterrestrial civilization had evolved 1 million years ago?

3. What's wrong with the definition "the past consists of those events that have already happened"?

EVENTS ON EARTH AND MARS

Elsewhere

22 min

11 light-minutes

Earth

Mars

This diagram illustrates the idea of the **Elsewhere**. The Elsewhere is a region of spacetime that is neither past nor future. The elsewhere of a given event consists of those events that cannot influence or be influenced by the given event – namely, those events that are far enough in space that not even light can travel between them and the given event.

The distance between Earth and Mars is 11 light-minutes. Events on Mars cannot influence events on earth for a period of 11 minutes. Events on Earth cannot influence events on Mars for a period of 11 minutes. Thus there is a 22 minute interval in which events on Mars cannot influence or be influenced by the present moment on Earth. These Martian events lie in the **elsewhere** of Earth's present.

Faster than Light?

0.8c

0.8c

Speed of small ship
relative to Earth?

~~1.6c~~   0.97c

In this diagram, the large ship is moving at 0.8c relative to Earth. The small ship is moving in the same direction, but at 0.8c relative to the large ship. Classical physics states that their velocities should be added together in order to find out how fast the small ship is moving relative to Earth. This simple addition would give the answer of 1.6c which is faster than the speed of light. Relativity shows that velocities do not combine in a simple addition, but in a more complicated way that does not allow a velocity combination to exceed the speed of light. In this case, the two velocities combine to produce a velocity for the small spaceship of .97c relative to Earth.

Lecture Eleven—Transcript
Faster than Light? Past, Future, and Elsewhere

Welcome to Lecture Eleven. My title "Faster than Light? Past, Future, and Elsewhere," draws on two of the problems that arise from the kinds of things we've been discussing. The nonrelative it, the relative it, relativity of simultaneity, for example. The fact that events that are simultaneous in one frame of reference are not simultaneous in another, and, in fact, that the time order of those events is also relative. Event A may occur before event B in one frame of reference. And event B before event A in another frame of reference.

How can these things be? They're closely tied with our notions of the past and the future and what those concepts really mean. They're also closely tied with a question that arises frequently when people study relativity. And that is why is it that nothing can go faster than light? I haven't asserted that fact yet, but it's been in the back of my mind in a lot of the things I've been saying, and now we need to bring it to the forefront.

So today's lecture deals with these two questions. What do we really mean by the past and the future? What about causality in a world where the time order of events can be different? And what about this business of faster than light? And how is that coupled with questions of causality?

I want to begin by clarifying a definition I gave you several lectures ago. And that's the definition of an event. In relativity, events are the key things. Events really happen. You were born. That happened. Different observers may disagree about the time interval between your birth and your sitting here watching this course, or listening to this course, for example. But nobody disagrees about the event of your birth having happened. An event is specified by giving the place it happened and the time it happened, and that is complete and enough to specify the event. We'll be talking, again, a lot about events.

Now, we saw several lectures ago that the time interval between two events is a relative quantity. Time intervals are simply not absolute. The time interval between your being born and your sitting watching this course might be, say, 45 years—that is, in a frame of reference at rest with respect to the Earth. But to somebody whizzing by Earth in a high speed spaceship going in uniform motion, straight-line motion at constant speed, that interval may be a very different amount of time. Time intervals are relative. That's something we came to a while ago, and I hope you're a least a little bit comfortable with that by now, even though, again, it is never going to make intuitive sense, because intuitive sense is common sense, and common sense, again, is built on that limited experience we talked about before.

But in the last lecture we came up with an idea that's perhaps even more radical. And that's the notion that the time order of events may be different in different frames of reference. And I left us last time with a question: How is that possibly consistent with our notions of cause and effect? How can the time order of two events be different? How can observers disagree about whether event A occurred before event B, or event B occurred before event A, when we expect of cause and effect that the cause comes before the effect? Surely your being born was a cause of your now watching this course. If you hadn't been born, you certainly would not now be watching this course. Don't observers all have to agree that your birth came before your watching this course? Well, the answer to that question is yes. There are only some kinds of events, only some events, only some pairs of events, for which the time order can be judged to be different by different observers.

I want to tell you a little bit more about what those kinds of events are. The events for whom the time order can be relative are a special class of events that are so far apart in space, in some frame of reference—and this then turns out to be true in all frames of reference—if they are so far apart in space that not even light, emitted at the time of this event, can get to the second event. If events are that far apart, then it turns out that there are different observers who will see the two events as event A occurring before event B, another observer will see event B occurring before event A, and there'll be other observers who see events A and B as being simultaneous. It's that class of events—events that are so far apart, that are widely spaced in space, that not even light can get from one event to another—those events are close enough in time that for some observers they occur at the same instant. They're simultaneous. And for some observers, event A occurs before event B, and for some observers event B occurs before event A. Now, we're beginning to get out of the realm where everything I say about relativity is going to follow absolute logic. So I'm not going to prove that statement to you. I'm simply going to assert it. It takes a relatively small amount of algebra to demonstrate it, but I'm not going to do it. So, you'll have to take this somewhat on faith—the statement that the events for whom the time order can be different for different observers are the set of events for which the distance between the events is so far, so great, that not even light could travel from one event to the other.

Let's go back to the example of your being born. And then you're sitting here, looking at this course, or listening to this course. How far apart are those events? Well, in space, those two events both take place on Earth. So, they're at most, thousands of miles apart. Could light, traveling at 186,000 miles a second, have traveled from the event of your birth to the event of your sitting here now? Well, it could have done so in a tiny fraction of a second. And, yet, maybe 45 years have elapsed. So light has had plenty of time to get from the event of your birth to the event of your sitting here now. Those are events for which the time order cannot be different for different observers. All observers will say, for those events, those events are close together in space and far apart in time. They're 45 years apart in time, judged by an observer on Earth. They're a few thousand miles apart in space, which is a very short distance in terms of how far light can travel in 45 years. Those events are, again, close together in space, far apart in time. No observer will think or measure that your sitting here watching the course occurred before your being born. All observers will agree that you were born before you watched this course.

Not all observers will agree that the interval between your birth and your sitting here now is 45 years, however. For some, that interval will be shorter. It depends on their relative motion, relative to Earth. But, all will agree that the event of your birth comes before the event of your sitting here now.

On the other hand, consider another case of some events. Consider an event that's happening right here, now. You're sitting watching this video and an event that happened at the time of your birth, but in the Andromeda Galaxy, which is 2 million light years a way. Now you were born 45 years ago, say. Well, light leaving the event of your birth could travel a maximum distance of 45 light years. Why? Because a light year is the distance light travels in one year. In 45 years, light travels 45 light years. Remember, a light year is a unit of distance, it's a unit of how far things are separated, and it's measured by how far light goes in one year.

So, in 45 years, light that left the event of your birth could travel 45 light years. Well, that's nowhere near as far as Andromeda, which is 2 million light years away. And, therefore, the event that occurred 45 years ago at the time of your birth, on Andromeda, and the event of your sitting here now watching this course, those two events are events that there could be observers disagreeing about when they occurred—which one occurred first. They won't only disagree about the time interval between them, they will disagree about which one came first.

There are observers for whom the event that occurred 45 years ago on Andromeda actually occurred first. And you might say, "Well, didn't it really occur 45 years ago." Well, if you start using that dangerous word "really," you're saying, oh, there's something special about the frame of reference of Earth and Andromeda, and observers moving relative to them are in weird, special frames that don't really count, and so, things aren't right for them. You can't do that. Relativity is the statement that the laws of nature, the laws of physics, are the same for all observers in uniform motion. So, everybody has to agree about that. So, everybody has equal perspective on deciding which event came first. And people disagree about that. Observers disagree about that. In fact, there will be some observers, moving in just the right way relative to Earth and Andromeda, for whom the event of your birth and the event of your sitting here now, and the event that occurred on Andromeda 45 years ago, as far as the Earth frame is concerned, that those events are simultaneous for some observers. They occur at the same time. And, again, for some observers, your sitting here now comes first. For other observers, that event comes first.

There's no contradiction of causality. Why not? Because of that fact that I'm going to discuss at great length in the second half of this lecture, the fact that nothing can go faster than the speed of light. In particular, no information can go faster than the speed of light. And because of that, for events that are so widely separated in space that not even light can get from one event to the other, there is no way for the events to communicate; there is no way for them to be causally related. And, therefore, there is no contradiction with some observers seeing event A before event B, and some observers seeing event B before event A. The events simply cannot be causally related.

I want to explore that situation in a little bit more detail with a specific example. In the late 1990s, we sent a wonderful space mission to Mars, and we landed a little Rover on the planet Mars. And you may remember the news at the time. The Rover was rolling around planet Mars, backing up to rocks, sticking its spectrometer into the rocks and analyzing them, and so on, and having a great time rolling around the surface of Mars and taking pictures.

At the time that happened, Mars and Earth were 11 light minutes apart. What's a light minute? Well, again, it's a unit of distance. It's the distance light travels in a minute. You can figure out what that is in miles by multiplying 186,000 miles a second by 60 seconds, and whatever that comes out, that's how many miles in a light minute. But it's just easier to talk about light minutes. Mars was 11 light minutes from Earth at the time that the Mars Rover was running around on the surface. Because Mars and Earth are both in orbit around the sun, they don't stay 11 light minutes apart all the time. But that was the distance, at that time.

What does that mean? It means it took 11 minutes for radio signals from Earth to get to Mars to tell the Mars Rover what to do. And it took 11 minutes for images being sent back by radio from the Mars Rover to get to Earth, or warnings that we got a problem—our computer is shutting down, as it did several times, or whatever—to be sent back from Mars. Eleven minutes is the communication time using light or other electromagnetic waves between Earth and the Mars Rover.

Well, I have a picture here that shows Earth and Mars and shows that they're 11 light minutes apart. And I'm showing, in addition to this picture, a couple of clocks—one on Earth and one on Mars. And we're going to assume that Earth and Mars are essentially at rest with respect to each other. That's approximately true. Not exactly. Their relative speeds are some tens of miles a second. And that's so small compared to the speed of light that for all practical purposes, as far as relativity is concerned, they're essentially at rest with respect to each other. They define the Earth-Mars reference frame then. And so these two clocks I've drawn are synchronized in that frame of reference. They both read the same time at the same instant. We talked about that in some detail last time. And we know how to synchronize the clocks.

Now, here's the issue. Suppose something bad is going to happen on Mars in 5 minutes. Here we are, we're sitting in the command center for the Mars Rover, and suppose a giant boulder is going to come rolling down and crush the Mars Rover, or one of those aliens we're looking for is going to emerge from a crack in the Martian surface and reach out and grab the Mars Rover and crush it. Is there anything we can do to stop that? Is there any way we can affect that event? Is there any way we can influence it? That event is going to occur 5 minutes from now. It hasn't happened yet, at least in our frame of reference—in the Earth-Mars frame of reference. It's going to happen 5 minutes from now. Is there any way we can influence that event? Well, if we know about that event, right now, it's the first time we know about it. There is no way we can affect it. There is no way we can stop it. We can send a message to the Mars Rover and say, hey, boulder is going to fall on you. But the Mars Rover will not get that message for 11 minutes. And the boulder is going to fall and crush it 5 minutes from now. Or, watch out, alien coming out of the cracks, going to get you in 5 minutes. That message is not going to get there in time. It's going to be 6 minutes late, because the shortest time a message can get from Earth to Mars is in 11 minutes—if you believe that nothing can go faster than light. And keep that question in the back of your mind, because I'll have more to say about that shortly.

So, my example would still be the case if it were 10 minutes before the alien was going to reach out, or the boulder was going to fall and crush the Mars Rover—even if we're 10.999 minutes. But, if it were 12 minutes from now, then we have the possibility of sending a message which will get there in 11 minutes, and the Rover has time to react and get out of danger. So that 11 minutes is an important break point. Events that are more than 11 minutes from now, in the future, on Mars, are events that we, here on Earth, can influence, because we can send a light signal, or a radio wave, or some other form of electromagnetic waves—the fastest things we have available to us or that any observer or experimenter or being anywhere in the universe has available to them. We can send a light signal or an electromagnetic wave of any kind, and we can warn the Mars Rover. And if the event is going to occur more than 11 minutes from now, the Mars Rover will get our warning and it can react—at least in principle.

What that means is this: There is a time span from now until 11 minutes from now—and I'm going to show that on the Mars clock—that we cannot influence, we can't affect events that are going to occur on Mars in the next 11 minutes. And again, I'm talking about during the era when the Mars Rover is on the surface, and Earth and Mars are 11 light minutes apart. There is a band of time, a band of events, that, as far as we are concerned, we, in the Earth-Mars frame of reference are concerned, have not yet happened. And yet, we can't influence them. Events beyond that time interval? Yep, we can influence them. But events in that 11-minute band, from now until 11 minutes in the future, we can't influence.

Now, what if we're sitting here in Mission Control for the Mars Rover and, in fact, that boulder is not going to crush the Mars Rover 5 minutes from now, but it crushed it 5 minutes ago? Are we unhappy? No, because we don't know that yet. The Mars Rover signal—we're still getting signals from the Mars Rover, they're signals that left 11 minutes ago and 11 minutes ago was before the Mars Rover got crushed by the boulder. It will be a while before we'll learn the bad news. It takes time for information to travel, because the fastest rate it can travel in the universe is c, the speed of light. So, an event that occurred 5 minutes ago on Mars, similarly, cannot influence the here and now on Earth. It can't influence us in the present. Later on we'll know about that event—the event of the Mars Rover getting crushed 5 minutes ago is not lost forever to us. We'll know about it sometime, and then we'll be very unhappy. Or the computer fails, or whatever else goes wrong—something bad happens to Mars Rover 5 minutes ago, we do not know about it now. We can't do anything about it. Not only that, we don't even know about it. It can't affect us in any way. It doesn't make us unhappy. It doesn't make Congress cut NASA's budget. It doesn't make anything happen right now. It may in the future. But right now an event that occurred 5 minutes ago on Mars has absolutely no influence on us. And, in fact, if you think about it, an event that occurred 9 minutes ago on Mars, or 10 minutes ago on Mars, or 10.99 minutes ago on Mars, those events cannot influence the present event here on Earth.

An event that occurred 12 minutes ago on Mars or 11.1 minutes ago on Mars, we can know about those. If the Rover was crushed 11.1 minutes ago, the signal has gone dead already. And we know that. So, events that occurred beyond 11 minutes ago, they can influence us. But there is a band from now to 11 minutes in the past that cannot have an influence on us. And, consequently, there is a band that extends 22 minutes in extent—from 11 minutes ago to 11 minutes into the future of events on Mars—that can have no causal relationship to events on Earth. Why? Because if they're in the past, the light or other information coming from them to tell us about them has not had time to reach Earth. If they're in the future, signals from Earth have not had time to reach Mars and affect those events. And so, those events are, in a sense, out of touch with the present event on Earth. There is a band at Mars, which is 22 minutes wide, which has no causal relationship to events on Earth. Those are the events that are far enough away in space—11 light minutes in this case—and close enough in time—within plus or minus 11 minutes of time from the present event here on Earth—that that causal influence can't exist. Because to have a causal influence, we need to send information telling the Mars Rover to do something, or it needs to send us information telling us it's got troubles or whatever. And in that band—22 minutes wide, plus or minus 11 minutes from now— that causal influence cannot happen, because no influence can travel faster than the speed of light.

So, that's the situation with the Mars Rover. And the events, event A—the here and now on Earth, in the control room of the Mars Rover—and event B—any event in that 22-minute window, centered plus or minus 11 minutes from right now on Mars, that's event B, any event in that window—those are the kinds of events that are far enough apart in space and close enough in time that some observers will see their time order differently. That event 5 minutes from now when the Mars Rover is going to get crushed, there could be observers moving uniformly through the solar system who would say that event occurs before the event of me sitting here right now in Mission Control for the Mars Rover. And there's no contradiction, because events cannot be causally related.

Similarly, there will be observers who say those two events are simultaneous. And there is no question of causality problems, because, again, they cannot be causally related. Events outside that

22-minute interval, it's a different story. They can be causally related.

Okay, well, let's expand this away from just Mars itself. Let's just talk a second about what we mean by the past and the future, in this context. If you ask a historian what the past is, the historian will tell you, it's all the things that have already happened. And what's the future? Well, it's all the things that haven't yet happened. But now we have an ambiguity, because we've got this range of time. On Mars it's 22 minutes wide. On the sun, which is 8 light minutes away, it's 16 minutes wide. At the center of our galaxy, which is 30,000 light years a ways, that band is 60,000 years wide, in time— 30,000 years before the present time, 30,000 years from the present time. In that band, events at the center of the galaxy are uninfluencable by events now on Earth, and events now on Earth can't be influenced by them.

In Andromeda, which is 2 million light years away, that band of time is 4 million years wide. That's the band in which events on Andromeda cannot be influenced by the present event on Earth, and they can't influence the present event on Earth. In a sense, those events are not in the past, because they can't influence the present here on Earth. And they're not in the future, because we can't influence them. They're in the *elsewhere*, as it's called in relativity. There's a band of time now, instead it's not just past and future anymore, there's not an abrupt demarcation. Instead, there's a new zone of time called the elsewhere. For Mars, when it's 11 light minutes from Earth, the elsewhere are those events that occur in a 22-minute-wide band, plus or minus 11 minutes from now. In a real sense, those events are not in the past or in the future. They're in this mysterious elsewhere—meaning they can have no causal relation to the here and now on Earth.

Now, don't get carried away by that strange word "elsewhere." It doesn't mean these events are lost forever. They are not connected to the present moment here on Earth. But if I wait a while on Earth, events that are in the elsewhere will become in my past. And a while ago, events that are now in the elsewhere were in my future. It's the present moment, the place and time of being here and now on Earth, that those events in that 22-minute band are in the elsewhere. They're not either in the past or future.

In fact, we really need to redefine what we mean by past or future. In relativity, the past becomes not the events that have already occurred because different observers disagree about that, at least for events that are far enough apart, and the farther away you go, as in the Andromeda case, the wider the span of time involved—4 million years for Andromeda, 22 minutes for Mars. We have to redefine the past as those events that can influence the present moment. And again, that's relative to the present moment and its place. The events in the past on Mars relative to the here and now, the present moments on Earth are those events that occurred more than 11 minutes ago on Mars.

What's the future? It's those events we can influence. On Mars, the future consists of all those events that are going to occur more than 11 minutes from the here and now on Earth. All observers will agree that the here and now on Earth occurs before those events. They may disagree about how much time has elapsed between the here and now on Earth and an event that we think occurs 12 minutes from now on Mars, but they will all agree that that event occurs later. They won't disagree about the time order of events that can be causally related, similarly, for the events in the past.

So, we have now a more complex picture of time. We have the past, the future, and the elsewhere. And they are all relative to that present moment.

All this depends on nothing moving faster than light. And that is one of the big questions that keeps coming up in relativity. Why can't anything move faster than light? Let me give you a few explanations for that. They all boil down, though, to the same thing. The principle of relativity says the laws of physics are the same for all observers in uniform motion. So, none of them goes beyond that. And every one of them is, therefore, logically as good as any other. And the first one is, in a sense, the least satisfying one. But it's also, perhaps, the most simple and profound.

The laws of physics are the same in all uniformly moving reference frames. One consequence of the laws of physics is that there should be light waves, and they should move at speed c. Therefore, all observers in uniform motion should see light moving at speed c. Therefore, there can't be an observer who's at rest with respect to light. Therefore, nobody can go at the speed of light. Now, that sounds a little tautological and trivial, but that's as good an explanation as we need. It isn't a very satisfying explanation, however.

And let me give you some more satisfying explanations, then. A little more technically—and this is the one Einstein worried about when he was 16 years old remember, Einstein worried what would happen if you ran along side a light wave at the speed of light. What would it look like? Well, he'd see a stationary wave. A wavy pattern that wasn't moving. But, a wavy pattern that isn't moving is not a solution to the equations of electromagnetism, to Maxwell's equations, it just isn't. That does not solve the equations. You plug the mathematical description of a nonmoving wave in, and it doesn't work. The only thing that works is a moving wave moving at speed c.

So, a stationary light wave is not a solution to Maxwell's equations. And yet, all observers in uniform motion have to have Maxwell's equations valid, because they have to have all the laws of physics valid. And therefore, there can't be an observer who sees a stationary light wave. Therefore, nobody can move along side a light beam. Nobody can move at the speed of light.

That's also not very satisfying, but it's at least an explanation. And it's an explanation based, ultimately, in principle of relativity that says all observers see the same laws of physics, including the consequence that the speed of light should be c.

Well, you might start thinking of cleverer ways to do this. One way you might think of, you know, those people movers in airports. Well, what if you put on top of one people mover another one, and another one, and another one. Couldn't you get up to speed c? Let me give you a picture that shows the same idea. Here we have a rocket ship going past Earth at 80 percent of the speed of light. Pretty fast. We've been using that hypothetical rocket ship before. Suppose— that's a big rocket ship, made as big as the planet Earth—suppose inside that rocket I build a smaller rocket. And I launch that smaller rocket at $0.8c$, relative to the big rocket. So I've got a small rocket that is barreling down the big rocket at $0.8c$ relative to the big rocket. Well, how fast is that small rocket going, relative to Earth then? Think about that a minute. Sure, it's going $1.6c$, right? It's going faster than light relative to Earth.

Sounds logical. But it's not true. In that particular case, the small ship is actually going about $0.97c$ relative to Earth. Why? Well, I'm not going to go through the mathematics of it, but just think a little bit about what's going on here. Measures of space and time in the big rocket ship that's going past Earth at 80 percent of the speed of light are different than they are on Earth. So, when I say the smaller rocket ship is going 80 percent of the speed of light relative to the big rocket ship, that does not mean it's going 1.6 times the speed of light relative to Earth. And, in fact, the equations that describe how velocities combine in relativity will never ever, ever let you go at speeds faster than light. In fact, if I replace the smaller rocket ship with a light beam going at speed c relative to the big rocket, those same equations will then tell me that light is not going at 1.8 relative to Earth, but it's going at exactly c relative to Earth as indeed we know it must, because the laws of physics, with their implication that the speed of light is c for all observers, must hold in all uniformly moving frames of reference.

So we can't get to speeds faster than light by leap-frogging ahead like this with multiple things going at faster and faster speeds relative to each other. Let me remind you here, although I'm talking about things like spaceships, and observers, and people, the real key in relativity is not that no object can go faster than light, but that no information can be transmitted faster than light. The maximum speed that information can be transmitted at is the speed of light. And it can be transmitted by the things that go at the speed of light, which may be only electromagnetic waves; there may be a few other kinds of entities in the universe—we're not sure—but whatever they are, they are massless entities, and they can go at the speed of light. But that's the fastest anything can go. And light is the only thing we really know for sure about that does that. And the speed of light is the upper limit to the speed at which you can transmit information.

So the key here is information. You cannot transmit information at speeds greater than c. And we're going to get back to that when we talk about a very peculiar quandary in quantum mechanics in one of the last lectures.

Now, is there something very special about light that is going on here? Be careful not to get too hung up on light. Talking about light gives us a lot of insights into relativity. But relativity isn't really about light. The constancy of the speed of light, or the sameness of the speed of light for everyone, is just a minor part of relativity. A minor consequence. What relativity is really about is space and time. In this case, in particular, about time. This business of trying to leapfrog the rocket ship is only one example. There are more mundane cases.

Suppose, for example, a police car is going down the road at 50 miles an hour. And I go past that police car. And the police car clocks me going 30 miles an hour relative to the police car. Can I get ticketed for going 80 miles an hour? Well, in practical terms, yes. But, actually, I'm not going 80 miles an hour relative to the road. I'm going 79.99 and a lot of nines and something, because velocities don't quite add the way you would expect them to. Why? Because the measures of time and space in the different frames of reference from which you are trying to add the velocities are not the same. The effect is negligible when we're talking about 50 and 80 miles an hour. But it becomes more and more dramatic as we talk about speeds close to c, and that's why in my spaceship case one spaceship going at $0.8c$ relative to another spaceship that was going at $0.8c$ relative to Earth, doesn't give me $1.6c$ relative to Earth. There's a law called the Relativistic Velocity Addition Law, and that's what, in fact, again, following from the principle of relativity, makes this all work out.

Now, let me add one important caveat before I finish here. People are often asking me, wait a minute, I just read an article. There actually was an article in recent years in one of the main physics journals. They showed a picture of a bicycle, and on the front it said, "Bicycling at the Speed of Light," because scientists had managed to get light to go as slow as 38 miles an hour. And they think they're going to have it down in a few years to one or two miles an hour in certain kinds of substances. There's nothing wrong with that. There's nothing wrong with light going slower in material media. When light goes through material substances, there's a complicated, electromagnetic interaction with the material and the light is slowed down. That's how your eye glasses work. That's how the lens of your eyes work. That's how my contact lenses are working. The light is slowed down. In the process, the light waves bend, and that's what allows us to focus light with lenses, for example. Light moves slower than c in material media. And there can be particles that move faster than light in those material media. In fact, when that happens, something analogous to the sonic boom of a supersonic airplane occurs, and it's called Cerenkov radiation. And we get a cone of bright light emitted by high energy particles that are moving, say, through water at speeds faster than the speed of light in water.

That's not a contradiction. The issue for us is the speed of light in vacuum. And that's the only real issue. In fact, a more sophisticated look at the speed of light, and if we had understood relativity intuitively when we started doing physics, this would be more obvious to us than what we have now. A more sophisticated way of looking at the speed of light, it's really a conversion factor between space and time.

We didn't really understand that space and time were as intimately related as relativity makes them. And it's c, it's the speed of light, that is the conversion factor between space and time, ultimately. And in the next lecture, we're going to look a lot more about that conversion factor between space and time. And the relation between the two. And we'll also give you a more physically satisfying explanation for why nothing can go faster than light. But, like all the other explanations, it's grounded in the principle of relativity—that the laws of physics are the same for all observers in uniform motion.

Lecture Twelve

What about $E=mc^2$, and Is Everything Relative?

Scope:

Shortly after publishing his 1905 paper on special relativity, Einstein realized that his theory required a fundamental equivalence between mass and energy. This equivalence is expressed in the famous equation $E=mc^2$. What this means is that an object or system of objects with mass m contains an amount of energy given by the product m multiplied by the speed of light squared. Because c is large, this is an impressive amount of energy. The energy contained in a single raisin could power a large city for a whole day.

It is commonly believed that $E=mc^2$ is about nuclear energy and that, therefore, Einstein's work is at the basis of nuclear weapons. Actually, $E=mc^2$ applies to all energy transformations. Most dramatic of these is the complete annihilation of matter and antimatter to produce pure energy.

The reverse aspect of mass-energy equivalence is that energy behaves like mass in making it hard to accelerate objects (remember Newton's law!). If you accelerate an object to high speeds, it gains a lot of inertia and becomes that much harder to accelerate further. This provides a more physically satisfying argument against reaching speed c: As an object's speed approaches c relative to you, its inertia increases without limit and would become infinite at c. Thus, it would take infinite force and infinite energy to accelerate any object to c, and that is impossible.

Is everything relative? No, the laws of physics aren't relative and, as a result, neither is the speed of light. Furthermore, there are other absolutes in relativity. One is the *spacetime interval* between two events—a kind of four-dimensional distance that is the same for all observers. In relativity, space and time merge into a single four-dimensional framework called *spacetime*. Different observers measure different times and distances between two events, but they all agree on the "distance," or interval, in spacetime.

Outline

I. Einstein's famous equation, $E=mc^2$, is mistakenly assumed by many to be the essence of relativity. Although the idea behind the equation is seminal, $E=mc^2$ came as an afterthought to special relativity, and it was not until 1907 that Einstein published a comprehensive paper on the subject.

   A. $E=mc^2$ asserts an equivalence between mass and energy. An object or system with mass m has an equivalent energy given by the product of m with the square of the speed of light. Because c is large, even a small mass is equivalent to a large amount of energy.

   B. $E=mc^2$ is commonly associated with nuclear energy, and Einstein's work is, therefore, mistakenly considered responsible for nuclear weapons.

   1. Actually, $E=mc^2$ applies to *all* energy transformations, including the chemical reactions involved in burning coal or gasoline or metabolizing your food, as well as the nuclear reactions that power the Sun or our nuclear reactors and nuclear weapons. Even a stretched rubber band weighs more than an unstretched one, because of the energy put into stretching it. Large-scale conversion of mass to energy occurs in the Sun, where nuclear fusion reactions convert some 4 million tons of mass every second as a result of nuclear fusion in the solar interior. Even with nuclear reactions, though, only a small fraction of the total mass is converted to energy.

   2. The most dramatic (and efficient) example of mass-energy equivalence comes from *pair creation*, the creation of a particle of matter and its antimatter opposite out of pure energy. The opposite process, annihilation, occurs when a particle and its antiparticle meet and disappear in a burst of gamma ray energy.

   3. A historical aside: Although $E=mc^2$ and Einstein are no more responsible for nuclear weapons than they are for the burning of gasoline in a car engine, Einstein did have a minor role to play in the development of nuclear weapons. Dr. Leo Szilard, a physicist who first conceived of a nuclear chain reaction, prepared a letter to President Franklin D. Roosevelt at the start of World

War II urging a U.S. nuclear weapons program to counter German nuclear efforts. Szilard convinced Einstein to sign the letter. This was Einstein's only involvement with nuclear weapons. Incidentally, Szilard later founded the Council for a Livable World, which has worked for decades to oppose nuclear weapons.

C. $E=mc^2$ provides another way of understanding why nothing can go faster than light

    1. Because of mass–energy equivalence, energy, like mass, manifests itself as inertia, making an object harder to accelerate.

    2. As an object is accelerated to high speed, its energy increases and, therefore, so does its inertia. The object becomes harder to accelerate.

    3. Inertia increases without limit as an object's speed approaches c. It would, therefore, take infinite force and infinite energy to accelerate a material object to the speed of light—and that is impossible.

II. Is everything relative, dependent on one's frame of reference?

  A. Believing that Einstein's work declares everything relative has sometimes been used to assert relativity in aesthetics, morality, and other humanistic areas. But even if everything in physics were relative, why should this carry implications for morality, for example?

  B. Clearly, everything isn't relative. The principle of relativity declares one absolute: the laws of physics. They are the same for everyone (at least, at this point, for everyone in uniform motion). A corollary of the laws of physics being absolute is that the speed of light is the same for all observers. So the speed of light is not relative.

  C. There are other so-called *relativistic invariants* that don't depend on an observer's frame of reference. An important case is the *spacetime interval* between two events. Although different observers get different values for the time between two events and different distances between the events, all agree on this interval, which is a kind of four-dimensional "distance" incorporating both space and time.

    1. An analogy—adapted from *Spacetime Physics*, by Taylor and Wheeler—is the measurement of distance between two points on Earth. To get from point A to point B, you might say "go 3 miles east, then 4 miles north." But suppose you made your map without correcting for the difference between magnetic and true north. Then, your map grid would be tilted, and you would describe the path from A to B differently, but the actual straight-line distance from A to B would be exactly the same.

2. Relativity is like that: Space is analogous to one direction, say east–west, and time, to the other (north–south). Different observers in relative motion are like the different mapmakers; each imposes a different "grid" on an underlying, objective reality. How that reality divides into space and time depends on the "grid"—that is, on the observer's state of motion, just as in the map analogy, the amount of eastward and northward motion differs with which map one uses.

3. There is an objective, absolute reality behind the quantities that are relative. In the map analogy, this is the distance from A to B, about which users of either map agree. In relativity, it is the spacetime interval between events.

4. Spacetime is the name for the four-dimensional framework in which physical events occur—a framework that transcends individual observers and their different reference frames and gives the lie to the notion that "everything is relative." In the words of Hermann Minkowski, who had been one of Einstein's mathematics professors and later worked on the mathematical aspects of relativity.

"Henceforth space by itself, and time by itself, are doomed to fade away into mere shadows, and only a kind of union of the two will preserve an independent reality." (Hermann Minkowski, 1908, as printed in Lorentz, et al., *The Principle of Relativity*, p. 75.)

Essential Reading:

Hey and Walters, *Einstein's Mirror*, Chapters 5–6.

Mook and Vargish, *Inside Relativity*, Chapter 3, Section 11; Chapter 4, Section 5.

Suggested Reading:

Moore, *A Traveler's Guide to Spacetime*, Chapters 9–10 (requires a lot of math!).

Taylor and Wheeler, *Spacetime Physics*, Chapter 1.

Davies, Paul, *About Time: Einstein's Unfinished Revolution*, Chapter 3.

Questions to Consider:

1. You throw a bunch of subatomic particles into a closed box, the walls of which block the passage of matter but not energy. Must the number of particles in the box remain the same? Explain.

2. A coal-burning power plant and a nuclear plant each put out exactly the same amount of energy each second. How do the amounts of mass that they convert to energy in the same time compare?

A Pair Creation Event

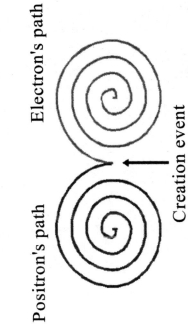

Electron's path

Positron's path

Creation event

Electron Inertia Increases With Speed

©2000 The Teaching Company Limited Partnership

Getting from A to B: The Invariance of Distance

In this first map, a mapmaker has chosen true north as his reference direction. His description of the distance from A to B is "4 units east and 3 units north"

In this second map, another mapmaker has chosen magnetic north as her reference direction. Her description of the distance from A to B is different than the description the first mapmaker gives. The second mapmaker's directions say "4.5 units east and 1.75 units north"

When we superimpose the two maps, we see that the actual distance between points A and B is the same in both maps. The directions differ from map to map but the underlying physical relationship between A and B remains unchanged.

Lecture Twelve—Transcript
What about $E=mc^2$, and Is Everything Relative?

Welcome to Lecture Twelve, whose title, again, consists of questions. First question, what about $E=mc^2$? And second question, is everything relative? Probably, there's no more famous equation than $E=mc^2$. And in the popular mind, $E=mc^2$ is the essence of relativity. Even in The Teaching Company's advertisements for this course, the headline is often $E=mc^2$. Actually, although $E=mc^2$ contains a fundamental and crucial idea, $E=mc^2$ was not part of Einstein's original 1905 paper on relativity. In a sense, it's an afterthought. Later in 1905, Einstein wrote a short paper that contained the essence of the idea about $E=mc^2$, but it wasn't until 1907 that he elaborated on that idea at some length. So, in some sense, the equation $E=mc^2$ and what it means are an afterthought to relativity.

You'll notice everything I've said so far about space, and time, and causality, and past, and present, and elsewhere, and future, and so on, is without any mention of $E=mc^2$. But when you begin to talk about relativity in terms of dynamics, in terms about the behavior of objects, and their energies, and so on, and forces that act on them, then you begin to worry about things that lead to the equation $E=mc^2$. So, I'd like to describe what that equation means. And I'd like to dispel a lot of popular myths about the equation as well.

What does $E=mc^2$ really say? Well, it asserts a fundamental equivalence between the two major things that make up the universe. What are the things that make up the universe? Well, there's matter, the solid stuff of that tabletop, and of the Earth, and of my body, and the more ethereal stuff of the air, which nevertheless consists of ultimately atoms of "solid matter." We know about matter. It's tangible. It's real. We can grab hold of it.

The other major stuff that makes up the universe is energy. And energy is a little bit less tangible to us. What is energy? Well, when I'm moving along, I've got energy. Energy is motion in a sense, or motion contains energy, or motion is a manifestation of energy. If I lift a heavy object up against Earth's gravity, like this, I've given it energy. There's energy there. If I stretch this piece of bungee cord, I've given it energy. If I have a light wave traveling from the sun to the Earth, the electric and magnetic fields that make up that light wave contain energy. And the light wave is carrying energy to Earth. In fact, it's the energy that keeps us alive here on Earth. And it's coming at a big rate—about 1,000 watts on every square meter of Earth's surface.

Energy is an important part of the universe. If there were no energy, everything would stop. Energy is important. And energy's the other stuff of the universe. And before $E=mc^2$, energy and matter were two separate things. There were separate physical laws describing how they behaved. Both of them are quantities that seemed to exist and never change in amount. If you have a certain amount of matter, you always have that much matter. It may change to different forms. You may burn hydrogen and oxygen, for example, and make water, but you've still got the same amount of matter, so it seemed.

If you have energy, it may change form. It may be electrical energy. You may put it into an electric stove and turn it into heat. You may put it into a microwave oven and turn it into microwaves, and the microwaves may go into a cup of tea and turn into heat. Energy transfers from one form to another. You may have it as the stored energy, ultimately electrical energy, in the bonds that make up the molecules of gasoline in the gas tank of your car, and then you step on the gas peddle and the gasoline burns. It's converted to a different form. The energy now is the energy of motion of your car, and of the heat coming out the exhaust pipe, and the heat going out the radiator, and the heat of friction, and all the other ways the energy in your car is, in fact, wasted. But, it's still there as energy.

So we had energy and matter. And we had separate rules describing their behavior. And one of the rules is that both of those things are basically conserved. If you have a certain amount of energy, you always have that amount. If you have a certain amount of matter, you always have that amount. Even though they may change forms.

What does $E=mc^2$ do for us? It asserts an equivalent between matter and energy. Between mass—if you will, weight, the measure of the stuff we have in matter—and energy. And what it says is this: It says that if I have a hunk of matter, this tennis ball say, and I take its mass, its weight basically, and I multiply it by the square of the speed of light—which is a great big number, because the speed of light is 300 million meters per second; 186,000 miles a second—I multiply the mass of this thing by the speed of light squared, I get a great big number. That's the energy equivalent of this tennis ball. If I could convert this tennis ball entirely to energy, I would have a huge amount of energy. And $E=mc^2$ says there is an equivalence and at least hints at the possibility of converting this tennis ball entirely to energy.

$E=mc^2$ says matter and energy are no longer distinct, separate substances that make up the universe, but that they are interchangeable. And $E=mc^2$ describes, if you will, the exchange rate between matter and energy. Just like you have the exchange rate between two different national currencies, now we have two different currencies, if you will, that carry the substance of which the universe is made—one substance, mass-energy, if you will—and there's a conversion factor between them. And the conversion factor is speed of light squared.

Again, I hinted last time that we should think of the speed of light, not so much as a speed, but as kind of a conversion factor between, ultimately, space and time. And coupled with that is speed of light squared becomes a conversion factor between mass and energy.

And as I pointed out, the speed of light is huge. The speed of light squared is even huger. And, consequently, the energy contained in ordinary matter is enormous. If I could somehow extract from an ordinary raisin all the energy it contains—annihilate the raisin completely and replace it with pure energy—I could power a great big city like New York for a day. So, if I wanted to build a raisin power plant, all I'd have to do is develop the mechanism that makes that conversion. And I'd go to the grocery store and I'd buy a box of raisins, which probably contains a few thousand raisins, which is probably enough for several years. And each morning I'd drop one raisin into my apparatus, and that's all it takes to fuel New York City if I could convert mass to energy with 100 percent efficiency. $E=mc^2$ tells us there is a tremendous amount of energy resident in all the matter around us.

Now, in the popular mind, $E=mc^2$ is associated with nuclear energy. And Einstein and his equation, the theory of relativity, are often held accountable for the existence of nuclear weapons. I remember watching a movie in eighth grade in which there was a nuclear explosion. And then in the aftermath of the nuclear explosion, Einstein's face came on the screen to imply: This is the man responsible for all of this. Well, that's nonsense. First of all, $E=mc^2$ is not only about nuclear interactions. It's not only about nuclear energy. It's about all energy. All energy and all mass are equivalent. Any time we do any process that results in a release of energy, we have decreased the mass, the amount of matter, in that system that released energy. Any time we do something that increases the energy of a system, that stores energy, we have increased the mass, increased the amount of matter, in that system.

Let me give you some examples. Many examples. I take a discharged battery, and I put it on a battery charger, and I charge it up. The battery weighs more after it's been charged. Not because I put any physical substance into it in the form of matter, but simply because it has more energy. You'll never notice that difference weighing it, because a battery is a very inefficient energy storage device and a very small amount of energy goes in there.

If I take material from a plant; if I take the carbon dioxide and the water that go into a plant, and with the light coming from the sun through photosynthesis then make more complicated molecules like sugars, and I weigh all the stuff that goes in—the carbon dioxide, the water—and I weigh the sugar molecule that's produced by photosynthesis, it weighs a tiny, tiny, tiny bit more. Insignificantly tiny bit for chemical reactions like that, because chemical reactions—no offense to the chemists—are rather weak and puny. But they convert matter to energy and vice versa.

When I burn gasoline in a car, the gasoline is converting some, a very small fraction, of its mass into energy. It's not just nuclear reactions. When I blow up a nuclear bomb or run a nuclear power reactor, I'm also converting matter to energy. And the only difference with nuclear reactions is I'm converting a much larger fraction—about 10 million times more mass gets converted to energy in a nuclear reaction than it does in a chemical reaction. It's still a very small and insignificant amount—less than a percent. Nuclear reactions are not very efficient converters of mass to energy. Even though they are about 10 million times more efficient than chemical reactions.

In fact, if you do something as simple as burn a candle. And you weigh the candle before you light it. And you weigh all the oxygen that combines with the wax from the candle as it burns. And you weigh all the soot and all the carbon dioxide that's produced as a result of that burning. You will find the products of that combustion weigh less than what went into it by a very small amount. But that small amount, when multiplied by c^2, tells you the energy that was released from the candle in the form of light and heat, for example.

Similarly, if you take two electric power plants that produce the same amount of energy, the same amount of power—1,000 million watts is a typical large-size electric power plant. Take two—a 1,000 megawatt, a 1,000 million watt electric power plants. One burns coal or other dirty fuel (by the way, that contributes dramatically to global warming) and the other fissions uranium, it's a nuclear power plant. And for the coal burning power plant, you weigh all the coal that goes into it and all the oxygen that goes in to combine with that coal when it burns. And you weigh all the stuff that comes out the smokestack, all the soot that's carried away from the electrostatic precipitators that remove the particulate stuff from the air. And you weigh all the pollutants—everything that comes out the smokestack—all the carbon dioxide, what have you. You will find there is a slight difference in the weight. In over one year you can measure that difference between what went in and what came out. And if you multiply that difference by c^2, that will be the energy the power plant produced. Most of it, by the way, as waste heat that was dumped into a river, probably, or another body of water—some of it into the atmosphere—and about a third of it went out as electricity.

If you do exactly the same thing for the nuclear power plant, you weigh all the uranium that came in—there's no oxygen to weigh because there's no burning going on—you weigh all the uranium that came in and you weigh everything that comes out of the plant, which isn't very much. And you weigh the waste fuel that's left in the reactor after you're done. After a year, you will find that the weight or mass of that system has also gone down. And if these two power plants produce exactly the same amount of energy in a year, the difference will be exactly the same. They'll have lost exactly the same amount of mass.

That's the point I'm trying to make, that $E=mc^2$ is not just about nuclear physics, it's about all interactions that occur. And the nuclear power plant and the coal burning power plant lose the same amount of mass in a year—convert the same amount of mass to energy if they produce the same amount of energy. The difference is much, much more mass went into the coal burning power plant. A 1,000 million watt coal burning power plant typically burns about 10 to 15, 100-car trainloads of coal every week. The nuclear power plant, typically, uses a couple of truck loads of fuel every couple of years. That's the difference. That's that factor of 10 million in the efficiency of nuclear reactions and chemical reactions in converting mass to energy. But the process is, in principle, the same.

There is nothing intrinsically nuclear about $E=mc^2$. And I spent a lot of time on that, because it's a great misconception that $E=mc^2$ is about nuclear energy. If it took $E=mc^2$ to discover nuclear fission, for example, it would have taken $E=mc^2$ to discover fire. It is not necessary to understand relativity to make nuclear bombs unfortunately, or fortunately as the case may be. But it's also not necessary to understand relativity to burn a candle, or to metabolize food in your body, or to burn gasoline in your car. Yet all those processes involve the conversion of mass to energy, as described by the equation $E=mc^2$.

A couple of other examples. Our sun, which is really a large nuclear fusion reactor, has very inefficient nuclear reactions going on in its core. They're the reactions that, ultimately, produce the sunlight that I've described takes that eight minutes to get from the sun to the Earth and keeps us alive. The sun is converting about 4 million tons of its matter to energy every second. The sun is on a big weight loss diet, if you will. It's losing energy and is, therefore, losing mass because $E=mc^2$ and the mass loss rate is about 4 million tons a second. And if you multiply that by c^2, that's a big amount of energy coming out every second. It's about a one with 24 zeros after a 100-watt light bulb's worth, to give you an example.

So the sun is losing a lot of matter—four millions tons of mass every second. Even in situations where we're not burning something or undergoing nuclear fission or nuclear fusion, when we change the energy of a system, we alter its mass by, again, $E=mc^2$ or $m=E/c^2$. For example, I lift up this heavy ball, as I did before. Now the entire system—consisting of Earth and the ball and their gravitational field—has more mass than it did before. It has more energy because I lifted up the ball. It has more mass also. If I let the ball back down again, I get that mass back as energy.

We don't see the details of the energy conversion, but it's going on there. The mass is a very, very tiny fraction of the total mass of the system. It's a very inefficient process in that sense. But it's really happening.

Similarly, if I take this bungee cord, which I stretched for you before and stretch it again. Let's look at this bungee cord stretching in the context of $E=mc^2$. What happens when I stretch the bungee cord? Well, energy conversion processes in my body result in the metabolizing of my food. That actually lowers my mass somewhat, because I'm converting mass to energy. That energy manifests itself as motion as I pull against the bungee cord, you stretch it. If I weighed the stretched the bungee cord now, I would find it actually weighs a little bit more than it did before. How much more? Well, $E=mc^2$. So, $m=E/c^2$. I can tell you how much energy I put in by multiplying the force I pulled with by how far I pulled it. That's how we would do that. And if I take that number E, and I say $E=mc^2$, I divide E by c^2. I get a tiny, tiny number. That's the amount by which the mass of the bungee cord system changed.

Don't look for additional particles to have gone in there. I haven't added physical particles to it. What I've done is added mass in the form, ultimately, of the energy associated with the stretching of the molecules when I stretched the bungee cord. It's ultimately stored actually in electric fields, primarily because electric fields are what hold molecules together. So, even as simple an act as stretching this bungee cord, or stretching this rubber band, anything that stores energy in a system, also increases the mass of that system by an amount you can calculate from the equation $E=mc^2$.

Now, none of these processes I've described are very dramatically efficient at converting mass to energy. Even nuclear reactions convert, typically, less than a percent of the total mass present into energy. And for chemical processes, like the burning of gasoline or the explosion of a chemical explosive, those numbers are, again, down by a factor of 10 million, even lower. And then processes like lifting that ball or stretching the bungee cord are even less efficient in terms of the amount of the fraction of the total mass of the system that gets converted one way or another.

However, there are possible situations where we can convert matter to energy with 100 percent efficiency and back again. We see those situations in subatomic physics cases. And I'm going to show you an example now, which is a simulated picture of a reaction that occurs, actually, quite commonly in large particle accelerators where we accelerate high-energy particles to very high speeds.

So, let's look at this picture. This is a simulation of what's called a pair creation event. I want to show you what we have here. These two spirals, you see, are the tracks of two subatomic particles. One of them is the very familiar electron, which is the particle that circulates in the outer parts of atoms. We'll get to that more in subsequent lectures. And the other is a particle called a positron, which is exactly like an electron, except it carries a positive charge. It's the electron's *anti-particle*. There exists something called *anti-matter*, and every subatomic particle we know about has an anti-particle, which is its anti-matter opposite. It's just like it, except it's opposite in crucial properties like electric charge.

Now, it's a remarkable fact that we can actually see the tracks of individual subatomic particles. The way we do that, they come out in these experiments with very high energies, and they move through a medium like liquid hydrogen, or they move through an array of wires that can detect the passage of their electric charge. And from that, either they disturb atoms along the way or they disturb these wire detectors. And we can piece together what the paths of these subatomic particles look like. And what we're seeing here is a situation where there is a magnetic field. Remember, magnetism and electric charge are intimately related. There's a magnetic field that's actually coming perpendicular to the picture, if you're seeing this in your book, or perpendicular to the screen. And that magnetic field causes the positron and the electron to go in spiral paths. And they spiral, in fact, in opposite directions, because they have the opposite electric charge.

So, there is the electron's path. And there is the positron's path. Now, what happens at the middle, where those two paths join? Well, that's actually a creation event. What has happened at the middle is that that electron and positron have been created out of, well, I want to say nothing. But it's not quite nothing. They've been created out of pure energy—pure energy in the form here of a burst of very high energy electromagnetic waves called a gamma ray—suddenly cease to exist, and in its place appeared a pair of particles, a pair of matter particles—an electron and its anti-matter opposite, a positron.

We haven't created anything new. In the old days, before we knew about $E=mc^2$, we would say, "Oh, we've created matter out of nothing." Well, we haven't created it out of nothing. What we've shown here is there's an equivalence between matter and energy.

And we have created matter out of energy. We haven't created electric charge, which really is conserved and can't be changed because we've created the negative charge of the electron and the positive charge of the positron. And the total charge is still zero, which it was before. So that's okay, but we have created mass—matter where there wasn't any before—out of pure energy.

So that's a pair creation event. And that's a 100 percent conversion of energy to matter. We can go the other way too. If an electron and a positron come together, they will annihilate completely and they will send out two bursts in opposite directions of gamma rays, of high-energy electromagnetic waves. And those waves will have a characteristic energy. The energy will be exactly the energy associated with $E=mc^2$ operating on an electron's mass. And, in fact, there are places in the universe where dramatically high energies exist, and where this annihilation process is occurring all the time. And we can identify it by looking at the gamma radiation, the gamma rays, with that particular energy. So this is something that does occur in the universe, and it's a 100 percent conversion of matter to energy.

In order to make my raisin-powered power plant, what I'd have to do is actually go to the grocery store and buy a box of raisins. And then I'd have to go to an anti-grocery store in some anti-matter world, if such a thing exists. We don't think it does. But if it did, I'd have to buy a box of anti-raisins. I'd have to very carefully keep them from touching any matter, and then, somehow, I'd have to drop a raisin and an anti-raisin into my power plant. And poof, they would annihilate in a burst of energy. Or my tennis ball, which I argued had some energy; in fact, a big amount, by $E=mc^2$. If I brought it together with an anti-tennis ball, then I'd have a 100 percent conversion of matter to energy. That's not a process we operate on Earth at any but the smallest scales in our atomic particle accelerators. But it is a process that, in principle, can occur, and it does occur in some places in the universe.

In fact, in the very early universe, the early fraction of a second of the existence of the universe, the temperatures were so high—and temperature corresponds to the motion of particles—that the particles moving around were moving so fast, that when they collided with each other, the collisions often involved energies bigger than that needed to create new particles. And so, in the very early universe, the number of particles, which we think of as sort of fixed here on Earth except for rare events in our particle accelerators or in cosmic ray interactions, we don't see this annihilation or this creation of pairs of particles, but in the very early universe that was very commonplace. And the number of particles simply wasn't fixed as there was an interchange between matter and energy. Now the universe has cooled to the point where that's a relatively rare thing; either here or even out in astrophysical situations. But it can occur, and it causes a 100 percent conversion of matter to energy—or the opposite.

Let me give you just a brief historical aside on this question of nuclear weapons and $E=mc^2$. Although Einstein was not responsible for nuclear weapons, and $E=mc^2$ has nothing to do with them, Einstein played a minor role in the development of nuclear weapons. Leo Szilard, who was a physicist who first conceived the idea of nuclear fission, actually suggested to Einstein that he write a letter to Roosevelt, President Roosevelt, saying that the U.S. should get to work on a nuclear bomb, because the Germans were, in fact, working on one at the start of World War II. And so Einstein agreed to sign this letter, and that helped get the U.S. Manhattan Project going. So there is a slight involvement of Einstein there, but it has really nothing to do with $E=mc^2$. Later, incidentally, Szilard founded the Council for a Livable World, which is an organization that has worked to oppose nuclear weapons.

One more aspect of $E=mc^2$ before we go on. Because energy and mass are, in some sense, equivalent, if I have energy, it exhibits an important property of mass—which is a property we talked about in the context of Galileo—and that is *inertia*. It's hard to accelerate energy as well as mass. And so if an object starts getting accelerated; it's now going faster; it has more energy; it has more inertia. And, therefore, it gets harder and harder to accelerate. And if we measure the inertia of, say, an electron, it looks something like this. I'm going to show you a graph with the electron's inertia as a function of its speed. An electron starts out with its normal inertia at slow speeds. But as the speed increases, the electron's inertia, and anything else's inertia, increases enormously. That makes it harder to change its motion, and harder and harder to accelerate it. So, if you want a more physical argument for why nothing can go faster than light, the argument is, as things get closer and closer to the speed of light, relative to you, they have enormous amounts of energy. And that enormous amount of energy corresponds to an enormous amount of inertia. And it makes it harder and harder to accelerate them. And it would take an infinite force, and an infinite amount of energy, to get anything up to the speed of light.

I think that's a more satisfying answer as to why you can't get to the speed of light. But it really is based in nothing more than anything else we've said, namely, the principle of relativity.

Finally, in the remainder of this lecture, the last one on special relativity, let me move on to one last question. Is everything relative? People have said, "Yeah, relativity says that everything is relative," and they even used that to justify moral relativism, and relativism in philosophy, and relativism in aesthetics. I think that's all nonsense. For two reasons, one is I don't think the physics of relativity has much to do with those other disciplines, at least in terms of making value judgments for them. And second, everything is not relative. Clearly it's not. The essence of relativity is not that everything is relative, but that some things aren't relative. What isn't relative? The laws of physics. They're the same for all observers in uniform motion. What else isn't relative? The speed of light is a consequence of the laws of physics being all the same. And there are other quantities that aren't relative as well. And I want to describe one of them in some detail.

I'm going to use an analogy here, which comes from, quite literally, from a wonderful book called, *Spacetime Physics,* which is in your bibliography. It's a delightfully written book by Taylor and Wheeler, who are experts on relativity. It's at a little bit higher level than this course, but it's worth looking at. And Taylor and Wheeler use an analogy of mapmakers. And these map makers are going to ask about the distance between two objects. So, let's look at a picture that shows that.

Here's point A and B, these are just points on the surface of the Earth. And I want to get from A to B. And one mapmaker lays out a map, a grid of north and south lines. It's based on true north. And in this mapmaker's system, we would say, "How do we get from A to B?" Well, we go one, two, three, four miles east, and one, two, three miles north. And that's how to get from A to B. And if we wanted to calculate the straight-line distance from A to B, it's the diagonal and it's exactly five miles. It turns out you can apply the Pythagorean theorem and get that.

Now, there's another mapmaker. He says, "I'm going to use magnetic north, which is not quite the same as true north, for my map." So the other mapmaker has a system that looks something like this. Here we have the same grid. One mile squares. North, east, south, west directions, but they're slightly different directions. Now how do you get from A to B? Well, a description would be go one, two, three, four, and about two-thirds miles east, and go about, oh, one-and-a-half miles north. And you got from A to B. That's a different description of how to get from A to B. Why is it different? Because the second map maker uses a different definition of north-south versus east-west. But we're still talking about the same underlying physical reality. And if this second mapmaker calculates the actual straight-line distance from A to B, it's still exactly what it was before. It's exactly five miles. And we can see that by imposing both mapmakers' systems on the same picture. The descriptions of how you get from A to B, in terms of how much eastward and how much northward you go, are different, but the description of the actual distance from A to B is one and the same.

Now, what's going on here? In a sense, the second mapmaker's map, it's east-west direction mixes in some of the north-south of the first mapmaker's map. East-west, north-south. Those are different dimensions, but they get kind of mixed up. Each mapmaker's north-south and east-west get mixed together to make the other map maker's east-west, north-south. That's why they have different descriptions of the same underlying physical reality. But the important point is it's the same underlying physical reality. The distance from A to B is invariant. It's the same no matter which mapmaker you use.

Now, what's this got to do with relativity? Well, the analogy is this: Space is analogous to one of these directions. Like, say, east-west. Time is analogous to the other direction. Say, north-south. Different observers in relative motion are like the two different mapmakers. They have different perspectives on what's east-west and what's north-south, or what are spatial intervals and what are temporal intervals. That's why different observers come up with different times between two events, and different spatial distances between them. Just like our two map makers come up with different amounts of east-west to go from point A to B and different amounts of north-south. But there's something they all agree on. And that something is a combination of, in the case of the mapmakers, east-west and north-south. They combine in a way to make an invariant—a true physical quantity that is objectively real and that they all agree on, and that's the distance between points A and B.

In relativity, it's a little bit different. In relativity, there's an objective, absolute "distance." But it's not a distance in space. It's a distance in space and time taken together. And if you combine those time intervals that we've been talking about between events that are different for different observers, and you combine that with the spatial interval between the two events, that's also different for different observers, every observer can calculate an invariant quantity. And it's called the *spacetime interval* between those two events. And they all agree on that spacetime interval. So, between two events, there is some reality in their separation. The reality is not a separation in space and a separation in time, like we thought it was before relativity. But it's a separation in a combined entity, which we're now going to call *spacetime*.

There really is a four-dimensional fabric to our universe. Four dimensions. The three dimensions of space—this way, this way, this way; three mutually perpendicular directions—combined with a fourth dimension, which I can't draw for you or indicate its direction, because I'm working in three dimensional space. But the fourth dimension is time. And the way spacetime breaks out into separate spaces and times differs with different states of motion. Just like the way physical reality of space for our mapmakers breaks out into north-south and east-west depends on their choice of compass directions. Similarly, what's space and what's time differs for different observers in different states of uniform motion. But they all agree on something underlying, which is the invariant spacetime interval. Now, you calculate it in a slightly funny way. Not the Pythagorean theorem, and I'm not going to get into that. But they all agree on that.

And there are, in fact, other quantities they all agree on. There are quantities that arise in electricity, for example, that involve the electric charge and the electric current that look different in different frames of reference. But they come together to form a common factor that everyone agrees on, no matter what their frame of reference. So there really is an underlying physical reality. And this underlying reality was summed up by Hermann Minkowski, who was Einstein's mathematics teacher, and later, as I said in an earlier lecture, became one of the people who gave the best mathematical interpretation of special relativity. And what Minkowski said was this, "Henceforth, space and time, by itself—space by itself, and time by itself—are doomed to fade away into mere shadows. And only a kind of union of the two will preserve an independent reality. And that union of the two is spacetime."

And we've just introduced it, now, as an abstract concept. But it's going to become a major player. It's going to play a major and active role in the development of general relativity, which is the next topic we'll be covering.

Timeline

1543 ....Copernicus publishes *De Revolutionibus Orbium Coelestium*, challenging the then-held view that Earth was at the center of the universe.

1686 ....Newton completes the *Principia Mathematica*, which includes his laws of motion and theory of gravity.

1801 ....Young's double-slit experiment shows that light is a wave.

1860 ....Maxwell completes the synthesis of the four equations of electromagnetism and shows that they imply electromagnetic waves that propagate at the speed of light.

1887 ....The Michelson-Morley experiment fails to detect Earth's motion through the ether.

1897 ....J. J. Thomson discovers the electron.

1900 ....Planck resolves the ultraviolet catastrophe by postulating quantization of the energy associated with hot, glowing objects.

1905 ....Einstein explains the photoelectric effect by proposing that light energy is quantized.

1905 ....Einstein publishes the special theory of relativity.

1911 ....Rutherford discovers the atomic nucleus and proposes his "solar system" model for the atom.

1913 ....Bohr publishes his quantum theory of the atom.

1916 ....Einstein publishes the general theory of relativity.

1919 ....Observations by Eddington and colleagues at a total solar eclipse confirm general relativity's predictions of the bending of light by the Sun's gravity.

1923 ....DeBroglie sets forth his matter-wave hypothesis. Compton effect experiment convinces most skeptics of the reality of quanta.

1927 ....Heisenberg states the uncertainty principle. Davisson and Germer show that electrons undergo interference, thus experimentally verifying DeBroglie's matter-wave hypothesis.

1929 ....Hubble discovers the expansion of the universe.

1932 ....Carl Anderson discovers the positron, verifying Dirac's hypothesis that antimatter should exist.

1939 ....Lise Meitner identifies the process of nuclear fission.

1948 ....Feynman, Tomonaga, and Schwinger produce the theory of quantum electrodynamics, successfully uniting special relativity with quantum mechanics.

1964 ....Quarks proposed as fundamental constituents of matter.

1965 ....Penzias and Wilson discover cosmic microwave background radiation.

1983 ....Experimental verification of electroweak unification.

1994 ....Existence of the top quark is experimentally verified.

1995 ....Second string theory revolution increases interest in string theory as a possible "theory of everything."

1998 ....Neutrinos found to have nonzero mass. Cosmic expansion of the universe found to be accelerating.

Glossary

Aberration of starlight: A phenomenon whereby a telescope must be pointed in slightly different directions at different times of year, because of Earth's orbital motion. The fact of aberration shows that Earth cannot drag with it the ether in its immediate vicinity and, thus, helps dispel the notion that ether exists.

Absolute motion: Motion that exists, undeniably, without reference to anything else. The relativity principle denies the possibility of absolute motion.

Big Bang: The explosive event that began the expansion of the universe.

Black hole: An object so small yet so massive that escape speed exceeds the speed of light. General relativity predicts the possibility of black holes, and modern astrophysics has essentially confirmed their existence.

Color force: The very strong force that acts between quarks, binding them together to form hadrons and mesons.

Compton effect: An interaction between a photon and an electron, in which the photon scatters off the electron, as in a collision between billiard balls, and comes off with less energy. The effect provides a convincing demonstration of the quantization of light energy.

Copenhagen interpretation of quantum physics: The standard view of the meaning of quantum physics, which states that it makes no sense to talk about quantities, such as the precise velocity and position of a particle that cannot even in principle be measured simultaneously.

Cosmic microwave background: "Fossil" radiation from the time 500,000 years after the Big Bang, when atoms formed and the universe became transparent.

Dark matter: Matter in the cosmos that is undetectable because it doesn't glow. Dark matter, some of it in the form of as-yet-undiscovered exotic particles, is thought to comprise most of the universe.

Electromagnetic wave: A structure consisting of electric and magnetic fields in which each kind of field generates the other to keep the structure propagating through empty space at the speed of light, c. Electromagnetic waves include radio and TV signals, infrared radiation, visible light, ultraviolet light, x rays, and gamma rays.

Electroweak force: One of the three fundamental forces now identified, the electroweak force subsumes electromagnetism and the weak nuclear force.

Elsewhere: A region of spacetime that is neither past nor future. The elsewhere of a given event consists of those other events that cannot influence or be influenced by the given event—namely, those events that are far enough away in space that not even light can travel between them and the given event.

Escape speed: The speed needed to escape to infinitely great distance from a gravitating object. For Earth, escape speed from the surface is about 7 miles per second; for a black hole, escape speed exceeds the speed of light.

Ether: A hypothetical substance, proposed by nineteenth century physicists and thought to be the medium in which electromagnetic waves were disturbances.

Event horizon: A spherical surface surrounding a black hole and marking the "point of no return" from which nothing can escape.

Field: A way of describing interacting objects that avoids action at a distance. In the field view, one object creates a field that pervades space; a second object responds to the field in its immediate vicinity. Examples include the electric field, the magnetic field, and the gravitational field.

Frame of reference: A conceptual framework from which one can make observations. Specifying a frame of reference means specifying one's state of motion and the orientation of coordinate axes used to measure positions.

General theory of relativity: Einstein's generalization of special relativity that makes all observers, whatever their states of motion, essentially equivalent. Because of the equivalence principle, general relativity is necessarily a theory about gravity.

Geodesic: The shortest path in a curved geometry, like a great circle on Earth's surface. Objects that move freely follow geodesics in the curved spacetime of general relativity.

Gravitational lensing: An effect caused by the general relativistic bending of light, whereby light from a distant astrophysical object is bent by an intervening massive object to produce multiple and/or distorted images.

Gravitational time dilation: The slowing of time in regions of intense gravity (large spacetime curvature).

Gravitational waves: Literally, "ripples" in the fabric of spacetime. They propagate at the speed of light and result in transient distortions in space and time.

Gravity: According to Newton, an attractive force that acts between all matter in the universe. According to Einstein, a geometrical property of spacetime (spacetime curvature) that results in the straightest paths not being Euclidean straight lines.

Hadron: A "heavy" particle, made up of three quarks. Protons and neutrons are the most well known hadrons.

Heisenberg uncertainty principle: The statement that one cannot simultaneously measure both the position and velocity (actually, momentum) of a particle with arbitrary precision.

Interference: A wave phenomenon, whereby two waves at the same place simply add together to make a composite wave. When both waves reinforce, the interference is said to be constructive and results in a stronger wave. When the waves tend to cancel each other, the interference is destructive. Interference is useful in precision optical measurements, including the Michelson-Morley experiment.

Length contraction: The phenomenon whereby an object or distance is shortest in a reference frame in which the object or the endpoints of the distance are at rest. Also called the *Lorentz contraction* and *Lorentz-Fitzgerald contraction*.

Lepton: Collective name for the light particles electron, muon, tau, and their associated neutrinos.

Mass-energy equivalence: The statement, embodied in Einstein's equation $E=mc^2$, that matter and energy are interchangeable.

Maxwell's equations: The four equations that govern all electromagnetic phenomena described by classical physics. It was Maxwell in the 1860s who completed the full set of equations and went on to show how they predict the existence of electromagnetic waves. Maxwell's equations are fully consistent with special relativity.

Mechanics: The branch of physics dealing with the study of motion.

Meson: A particle made up of two quarks (actually, a quark and an antiquark).

Michelson-Morley experiment: An 1880s experiment designed to detect Earth's motion through the ether. The experiment failed to detect such motion, paving the way for the abandonment of the ether concept and the advent of relativity.

Neutrino: An elusive particle with very small mass that arises in weak nuclear reactions.

Neutron star: An astrophysical object that arises at the end of the lifetime of certain massive stars. A typical neutron star has the mass of several Suns crammed into a ball with a diameter about that of a city.

Photoelectric effect: The ejection of electrons from a metal by the influence of light incident on the metal.

Photon: The quantum of electromagnetic radiation. For radiation of frequency f, the quantum of energy is $E=hf$.

Planck's constant: A fundamental constant of nature, designated h, that sets the basic scale of quantization. If h were zero, classical physics would be correct; h being nonzero is what necessitates quantum physics.

Principle of Complementarity: Bohr's statement that wave and particle aspects of nature are complementary and can never both be true simultaneously.

Principle of Equivalence: The statement that the effects of gravity and acceleration are indistinguishable in a sufficiently small reference frame. The principle of equivalence is at the heart of general relativity's identification of gravity with the geometry of spacetime.

Principle of Galilean Relativity: The statement that the laws of motion are the same in all uniformly moving frames of reference; equivalently, such statements as "I am moving" or "I am at rest" are meaningless unless "moving" and "rest" are relative to some other object or reference frame.

Quanta: Discrete, indivisible "chunks" of a physical quantity, such as energy.

Quark: A fundamental particle, building block of protons and neutrons, as well as all other hadrons and mesons. There are six different quarks, two in each of the three families of matter.

Relativistic invariant: A quantity that has a value that is the same in all frames of reference. The spacetime interval is one example of a relativistic invariant.

Relativity principle: A statement that only relative motion is significant. The principle of Galilean relativity is a special case, applicable only to the laws of motion. Einstein's principle of special relativity covers all of physics but is limited to the case of uniform motion.

Spacetime: The four-dimensional continuum in which the events of the universe take place. According to relativity, spacetime breaks down into space and time in different ways for different observers.

Spacetime curvature: The geometrical property of spacetime that causes its geometry to differ from ordinary Euclidean geometry. The curvature is caused by the presence of massive objects, and other objects naturally follow the straightest possible paths in curved spacetime. This is the essence of general relativity's description of gravity.

Spacetime interval: A four-dimensional "distance" in spacetime. Unlike intervals of time or distance, which are different for observers in relative motion, the spacetime interval between two events has the same value for all observers.

Special theory of relativity: Einstein's statement that the laws of physics are the same for all observers in uniform motion.

String theory: A description of physical reality in which the fundamental entities are not particles but tiny string-like loops. Different oscillations of the loops correspond to what we now consider different "elementary" particles. String theory is a leading candidate for a "theory of everything."

Time dilation: In special relativity, the phenomenon whereby the time measured by a uniformly moving clock present at two events is shorter than that measured by separate clocks located at the two events. In general relativity, the phenomenon of time running slower in a region of stronger gravity (greater spacetime curvature).

Ultraviolet catastrophe: The absurd prediction of classical physics that a hot, glowing object should emit an infinite amount of energy in the short-wavelength region of the electromagnetic spectrum.

Universal gravitation: The concept, originated by Newton, that every piece of matter in the universe attracts every other piece.

Wave packet: A construction made from waves of different frequencies that results in a localized wave disturbance.

White dwarf: A collapsed star with approximately the mass of the Sun crammed into the size of the Earth.

Wormhole: A hypothetical "tunnel" linking otherwise distant regions of spacetime.

Bibliography

To the Student/Reader: It is difficult to find readings that exactly parallel the structure of the lectures. The readings I've chosen are designed to extend and complement the lectures, rather than to repeat the lecture material. Most of the materials chosen, even those in the "Suggested Reading" category, are aimed at lay audiences. Motivated readers will find more in-depth and mathematically oriented coverage of these topics in science textbooks, especially at the college level. The books listed here include a mix of older and more contemporary works. Many good books on the development of modern physics are now quite dated and out of print, but they still provide excellent introductions to the subject. Books listed under "Essential
Reading" are in print as of 1999; some of the others are out of print but should be available in most public libraries. New books on the more contemporary subjects covered in these lectures are published each year.

Barrow, John D., and Silk, Joseph, *The Left Hand of Creation: The Origin and Evolution of the Expanding Universe* (Oxford University Press, 1993). This overview of cosmology, originally published in 1983 and updated ten years later, is particularly good on the relation between particle physics and cosmology.

Brennan, Richard, *Heisenberg Probably Slept Here: The Lives, Times, and Ideas of the Great Physicists of the 20th Century* (John Wiley & Sons, 1997). Part biography, part science, this book details the lives and contributions of Newton (even though he's not from the twentieth century), Einstein, Planck, Rutherford, Bohr, Heisenberg, Feynman, and Gell-Mann. Notably absent are the great female physicists of the century, most of whom made their contributions in nuclear physics: Nobel laureates Marie Curie (two Nobel Prizes) and her daughter Irène; Maria Goeppert Mayer, Nobel laureate for her contributions to nuclear theory; and Lise Meitner, who first identified the process of nuclear fission.

Casper, Barry, and Noer, Richard, *Revolutions in Physics* (New York, W. W. Norton, 1972). Used in college science courses for nonscience students, this well-written book describes a number of important revolutions in ideas about the physical world, including but not limited to those of modern physics.

Calaprice, Alice, ed., *The Quotable Einstein* (Princeton University Press, 1996). Need a quote by Einstein on your favorite subject? You'll find it all here—from religion to science to marriage to music to vegetarianism to abortion to capitalism to sailing, and much more!

Chaisson, Eric, *Relatively Speaking* (New York: W.W. Norton, 1988). Fairly up-to-date coverage of general relativity and its impact on contemporary astrophysics and cosmology.

Daintith, John, Mitchell, Sarah, Tootill, Elizabeth, and Gjertsen, Derek, *Biographical Encyclopedia of Scientists* (Institute of Physics Publishing, 1994). A handy source of brief biographical sketches of major scientists, both historical and contemporary.

Davies, Paul, *About Time: Einstein's Unfinished Revolution* (New York: Simon and Schuster, 1995). Davies, winner of the Templeton Prize for Religion, is a prolific popularizer of science and an active researcher in gravitational physics. This book takes the reader on an exploration of the nature of time, well beyond what's covered in this lecture series.

Davies, P. C. W., and Brown, J. R., eds., *The Ghost in the Atom* (Cambridge University Press, 1986). This book introduces the strange concepts of quantum physics and provides transcripts of question-and-answer sessions with some of the leading physicists concerned with interpretations of quantum physics.

Einstein, Albert, and Infeld, Leopold, *The Evolution of Physics*, (Simon & Schuster, 1967 and earlier editions). This old classic presents the conceptual background behind the development of relativity. Although not as lively as some contemporary works, it's good to hear about relativity in Einstein's own words (and those of his colleague, Infeld).

French, A. P., ed., *Einstein: A Centenary Volume* (Harvard University Press, 1979). This work was produced by the International Commission on Physics Education in celebration of the hundredth anniversary of Einstein's birth. The interested reader will find here a wealth of historical, biographical, and scientific perspective on Einstein's life and work, including translations of some original Einstein writings.

Fritzsch, Harald, *An Equation that Changed the World* (University of Chicago Press, 1994). There's more emphasis here than I would like on $E=mc^2$, but this book still provides a good introduction to relativity.

Greene, Brian, *The Elegant Universe: Superstrings, Hidden Dimensions, and the Quest for the Ultimate Theory* (W.W. Norton, 1999). This lively and very contemporary book is written at just the right level for a layperson interested in really understanding what string theory is about. Author Greene, himself a string theory researcher, concentrates on the revolution in string theory of the mid-1990s and communicates his enthusiasm for a theory he believes really has the makings of the "theory of everything."

Gribbin, John, *In Search of Schrödinger's Cat: Quantum Physics and Reality* (Bantam Books, 1984). A good book for nonscientists on the basics of quantum physics, which then goes on to give clear descriptions of such "quantum weirdness" as Schrödinger's cat and EPR experiments. As the paperback edition's cover says: "A fascinating and delightful introduction to the strange world of the quantum..."

Hafele, J. C., and Keating, Richard, "Around-the-World Atomic Clocks: Predicted Relativistic Time Gains" and "Around-the-World Atomic Clocks: Observed Relativistic Time Gains," *Science*, vol. 177, pp. 166–170 (July 1972). These back-to-back scientific papers describe in detail the background and experiments on relativistic time dilation using atomic clocks. Both special and general relativistic effects are covered. There's a good bit of math. *Science* is a general publication for scientists, so this is not just for relativity experts.

Han, M. Y., *The Probable Universe: An Owner's Guide to Quantum Physics* (Summit, PA: TAB Books/McGraw-Hill, 1993). This short book provides a brief introduction to the ideas of quantum physics, then goes on to its many contemporary practical applications, such as tunneling microscopy, microelectronic devices, and more. Color plates of tunneling microscope photos show just how far technology can go in manipulating individual atoms.

Hawkins, Michael, *Hunting Down the Universe: The Missing Mass, Primordial Black Holes and Other Dark Matters* (Little, Brown, 1997). This is a cosmology book with an emphasis on contemporary problems and observational evidence in cosmology.

Heisenberg, Werner, *Physics and Philosophy: The Revolution in Modern Science* (New York: Harper, 1962; also republished by Prometheus Books, Amherst, NY, 1999). In his later years Heisenberg turned increasingly to philosophical issues. This book sets forth his views, especially on the interpretation of quantum physics.

Hey, Tony, and Walters, Patrick, *Einstein's Mirror* (Cambridge University Press, 1997). Written in a breezy, popular style and prolifically illustrated, this book presents the ideas of relativity intermixed with lots of modern technology and astronomy. Not the most coherent presentation of relativity but fun to read.

—————, *The Quantum Universe* (Cambridge University Press, 1987). An exposition of quantum physics, stylistically very similar to the authors' relativity book described above.

Hoffmann, Banesh, *Relativity and Its Roots* (Dover reprint, 1999, or Freeman, 1983). The philosophy and organization of Hoffmann's book parallel this course fairly well, although Hoffmann goes into more mathematical depth and includes copious geometrical diagrams. Much of the heavier material is set aside in boxes, so the nonmathematical reader is free to ignore it.

Kaku, Michio, *Hyperspace* (New York: Anchor Books, 1994). Kaku, a prolific science writer, provides a trendy look at modern physics, emphasizing string theory and the search for a "theory of everything."

Kane, Gordon, *The Particle Garden* (Addison Wesley, 1995). In this book, Kane, a particle physicist and popular lecturer, gives a clear, nonmathematical explication of the standard model of particles and forces.

Lasota, Jean-Pierre, "Unmasking Black Holes," *Scientific American*, vol. 280, no. 5, p. 40 (May 1999). In this article, an astrophysicist presents contemporary evidence for the reality of black holes.

Lederman, Leon (with Dick Teresi), *The God Particle: If the Universe Is the Answer, What Is the Question?* (Boston: Houghton Mifflin, 1993). A Nobel laureate and former director of the Fermi National Accelerator, Lederman teams with Teresi, science writer and former editor of *Omni* magazine, in a lively look at the history and science of modern particle physics.

Lightman, Alan, *Ancient Light: Our Changing View of the Universe* (Harvard University Press, 1991). Lightman—scientist, science writer, and novelist—devotes a chapter to each of the main themes in modern cosmology. The book includes biographical sketches of leading cosmologists.

—————, *Great Ideas in Physics* (New York: McGraw-Hill, 1992). Lightman has chosen his favorite "big ideas" in physics. The sections on relativity provide good supplements to this course.

Lindley, David, *Where Does the Weirdness Go? Why Quantum Mechanics Is Strange but not as Strange as You Think* (Basic Books/HarperCollins, 1996). Lindley, formerly an astrophysicist at Cambridge and the Fermi National Accelerator Laboratory, later became an editor at the British science journal *Nature* and at *Science News*. *Where Does the Weirdness Go?* is an excellent introduction to quantum physics, with emphasis on such quandaries as Schrödinger's cat, EPR experiments, and the general philosophical interpretation of quantum physics.

Mather, John C., and Boslough, John, *The Very First Light: The True Inside Story of the Scientific Journey Back to the Dawn of the Universe* (Basic Books, 1996). Mather, Project Scientist at NASA for the Cosmic Background Explorer (COBE) satellite, teams with science writer Boslough to explore the science, politics, and personalities behind our most detailed knowledge of the cosmic microwave background radiation.

Mook, Delo, and Vargish, Thomas, *Inside Relativity* (Princeton University Press, 1987). A physicist and artist teamed up to ensure that this introduction to relativity would be truly comprehensible to nonscientists. And it is. It's not flashy, but it provides a good, solid introduction to the subject.

Moore, Thomas, *A Traveler's Guide to Spacetime* (New York: McGraw-Hill, 1995). Written as a textbook for a month-long relativity segment in sophomore-level college physics courses, this book is much more mathematical than others in this bibliography, but it provides a lively, clear, and very contemporary look at its subject. Readers wanting more math would do well to read Moore.

Padmanabhan, T., *After the First Three Minutes: The Story of Our Universe* (Cambridge University Press, 1998). An astrophysicist outlines the history of the universe. Includes good background material on star formation and other relevant astrophysical processes. The title is a takeoff on Weinberg's *The First Three Minutes*, listed below.

Pagels, Heinz, *The Cosmic Code: Quantum Physics as the Language of Nature* (New York: Simon and Schuster, 1982). This solid introduction to quantum physics for the nonscientist is, unfortunately, out of print.

Riordan, Michael, *The Hunting of the Quark* (Simon & Schuster, 1987). This book gives a history of particle physics, especially the quark concept, that emphasizes the personalities and interactions of the scientists and scientific teams involved in particle theories and experiments.

Sime, Ruth, *Lise Meitner: A Life in Physics* (University of California Press, 1996). A scholarly but eminently readable account of the life of Lise Meitner, the nuclear physicist who identified the process of nuclear fission.

Spielberg, Nathan, and Anderson, Byron D., *Seven Ideas that Shook the Universe* (Wiley, 1985). Among the "universe shaking" ideas covered in this book are some from quantum physics; see Chapters 7 and 8.

Taylor, Edwin, and Wheeler, John Archibald, *Spacetime Physics*, 2nd edition (New York: W. H. Freeman, 1992). John Archibald Wheeler of Princeton is one of the leading American physicists of the century. Wheeler and MIT physicist Edwin Taylor have produced a book aimed at college physics students but emphasizing the conceptual essence of relativity. Written in a lively but slightly quirky style, this book presents special relativity in a way that prepares the reader for the curved spacetime of the general theory. The authors do not avoid math, but the conceptual aspects of relativity are always in the forefront.

Thorne, Kip, *Black Holes and Time Warps: Einstein's Outrageous Legacy* (New York: W. W. Norton, 1994). Thorne, a leading researcher on black holes and general relativity, has written a lively and up-to-date book for nonscientists. A good introduction to relativity is followed by convincing arguments for why black holes must exist.

Weinberg, Steven, *The First Three Minutes* (Basic Books, 1988). A noted theorist and winner of the 1979 Nobel Prize for physics details the first few minutes of creation, when a lot of important events happened that set the stage for all that followed.

Will, Clifford, *Was Einstein Right? Putting General Relativity to the Test* (New York: Basic Books, 1986). This book explores experimental tests of general relativity, both the "classic" tests, such as the bending of starlight and early gravitational time dilation experiments, to the even more convincing results from modern astrophysics. Its 1986 publication date makes it a bit dated in this rapidly advancing field, but the essential evidence for general relativity is all there.

Wheeler, John Archibald, *A Journey into Gravity and Spacetime* (New York: Scientific American Library, 1990). Wheeler, described under Taylor and Wheeler, above, has written this "coffee table" book with plenty of color pictures and few equations. As in *Spacetime Physics*, the emphasis is on the essential conceptual basis of general relativity.

Wolf, Fred Alan, *Taking the Quantum Leap* (New York: Harper & Row, 1989). Wolf, a former physics professor from San Diego State University, has written yet another good introduction to quantum physics for the nonscientist. Wolf's book is particularly strong on the role of the observer in quantum measurements. Simple illustrations and catchy section titles help make this book an inviting introduction to the subject.